11+ Non-Verbal Reasoning

For the **CEM** test

These 10-Minute Tests from CGP are perfect for short bursts of 11+ practice — just what children need to keep their skills fresh in the run-up to the test.

Each test is packed with realistic CEM-style questions, with detailed answers at the back of the book. There's even a progress chart to keep track of their scores.

This is Book 2. For more quick-fire tests at the same level, don't miss Book 1!

10-Minute Tests

Ages
10-11

How to use this book

This book is made up of 10-minute tests and puzzle pages.
There are answers and detailed explanations in the pull-out section at the back of the book.

10-Minute Tests

- There are 31 tests in this book, each containing 18 or 19 questions.

- Each test is designed to cover a good range of the question styles and topics that your child could come across in the non-verbal reasoning sections of their 11+ test, at the same difficulty level.

- Your child should aim to score at least 16 in each 10-minute test.
  If they score less than this, use their results to work out the areas they need more practice on.

- If your child hasn't managed to finish the test in time, they need to work on increasing their speed, whereas if they have made a lot of mistakes, they need to work more carefully.

- Keep track of your child's scores using the progress chart on the inside back cover of the book.

Puzzle Pages

- There are 10 puzzle pages in this book, which are a great break from test-style questions. They encourage children to practise the same skills that they will need in the test, but in a fun way.

Published by CGP

Editors:
Marc Barnard, Alex Fairer, Katherine Faudemer, Sharon Keeley-Holden, Rachel Kordan

With thanks to Alison Griffin and Glenn Rogers for the proofreading.

Please note that CGP is not associated with CEM or The University of Durham in any way.
This book does not include any official questions and it is not endorsed by CEM or The University of Durham.
CEM, Centre for Evaluation and Monitoring, Durham University and *The University of Durham*
are all trademarks of The University of Durham.

ISBN: 978 1 78908 195 4
Printed by Elanders Ltd, Newcastle upon Tyne
Clipart from Corel®

Based on the classic CGP style created by Richard Parsons.

Contents

Question Type Examples

These pages contain a completed example question for each question type that appears in this book. Have a look through them to familiarise yourself with the question types before you do the tests.

Odd One Out

Find the figure in each row that is most unlike the other figures.

Example:

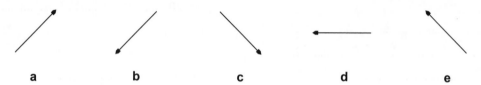

Answer: d

In all other figures, the arrow points diagonally.

Find the Figure Like the First Two or Three

Work out which option is most like the two or three figures on the left.

Example:

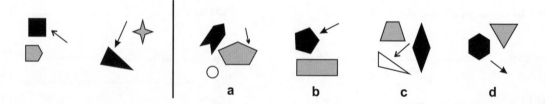

Answer: b

All figures must have an arrow pointing at a black shape.

Complete the Hexagonal Grid

Work out which of the options best fits in place of the missing hexagon in the grid.

Example:

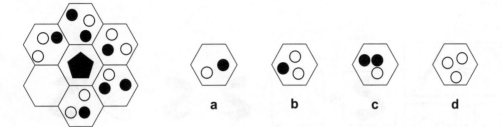

Answer: c

Going round the outer hexagons, the number of black circles alternates between one and two.

Complete the Square Grid

Work out which of the options best fits in place of the missing square in the grid.

Example:

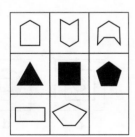

           a   b   c   d

Answer: c

Working from left to right, the number of sides of the shape increases by one in each grid square.

Complete the Pair

Look at how the first two figures are changed, and then work out which option would look like the third figure if you changed it in the same way. (In some questions just one figure will change into another. This figure will look like a bug.)

Example:

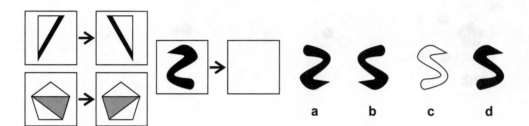

a	b	c	d

Answer: d

The figure reflects across.

Complete the Series

Work out which of the options best fits in place of the missing square in the series. (Occasionally, the series might be made up of two pairs of squares. These questions are solved in a similar way to Complete the Pair questions.)

Example:

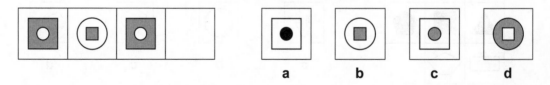

a	b	c	d

Answer: b

The figures alternate between a white circle in a grey square and a grey square in a white circle.

Work out which option would look like the figure on the left if it was rotated.

Example:

 Rotate

a   b   c   d

Answer: d

The figure has been rotated 90 degrees clockwise.

Work out which option would look like the figure on the left if it was reflected over the line.

Example:

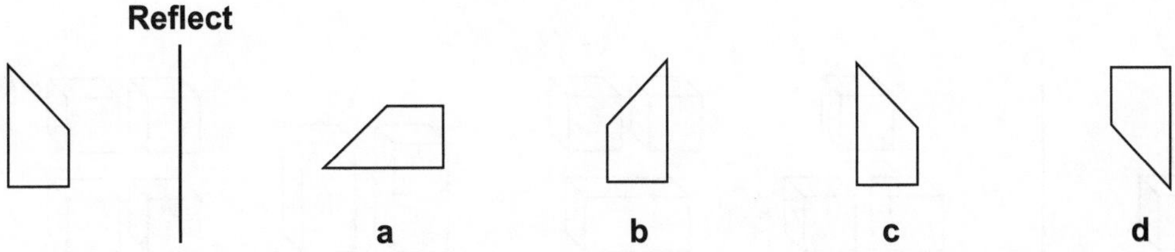

Reflect

a   b   c
d

Answer: b

Options A and D are rotations of the shape on the left. Option C has not been reflected.

3D Rotation

Work out which 3D figure in the grey box has been rotated to make the new 3D figure.

Example:

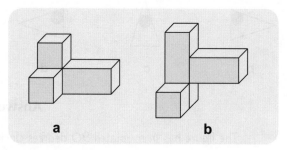

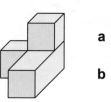

a

b

Answer: a

Figure A has been rotated 90 degrees right-to-left (see the glossary on page 142).

3D Building Blocks

Work out which set of blocks can be put together to make the 3D figure on the left.

Example:

 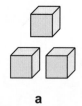 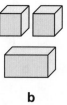 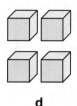

a   b   c   d

Answer: b

The block at the bottom of B rotates to become the block at the back of the figure. The two cubes move to the front.

Work out which option is a top-down 2D view of the 3D figure on the left.

Example:

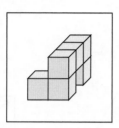 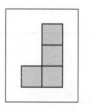 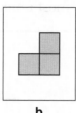 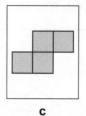 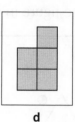

a   **b**   **c**   **d**

Answer: a

There are four blocks visible from above, which rules out options B and D.
There is a line of three blocks on the right-hand side of the shape, which rules out option C.

Cubes and Nets

Work out which of the four cubes can be made from the net.

Example:

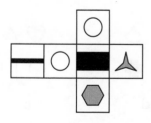

a   **b**   **c**   **d**

Answer: c

There is no black circle, which rules out option A. The thick black line and the thin black line must be on opposite sides, which rules out option B. There is only one grey hexagon, which rules out option D.

You have **10 minutes** to do this test. Circle the letter for each correct answer.

> Find the figure in each row that is most unlike the others.

1.

     a   **b**   **c**   **d**   **e**

2.

     a   **b**   **c**   **d**   **e**

3.

     a   **b**   **c**   **d**   **e**

4.

     a   **b**   **c**   **d**   **e**

Work out which of the options best fits in place of the missing square in the series.

5.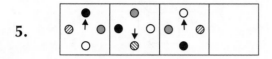

a   b   c   d

6.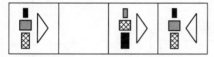

a   b   c   d

7.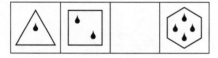

a   b   c   d

8.

a   b   c   d

9.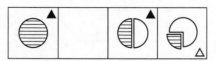

a   b   c   d

Test 1

Work out which 3D figure in the grey box has been rotated to make the new 3D figure.

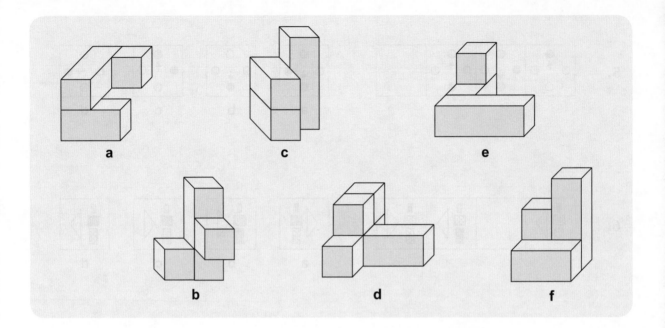

a

c

e

b

d

f

10.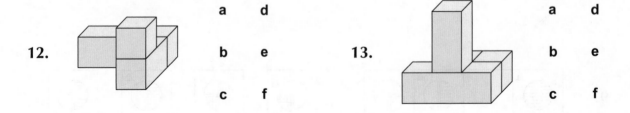

a   d

b   e

c   f

11.

a   d

b   e

c   f

12.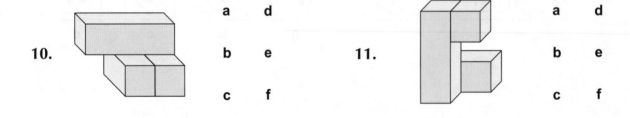

a   d

b   e

c   f

13.

a   d

b   e

c   f

Work out which option would look like the figure on the left if it was reflected over the line.

Reflect

14.

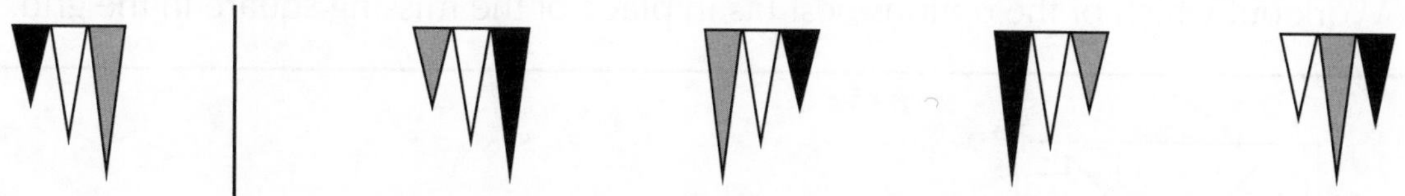

a   b   c   d

Reflect

15.

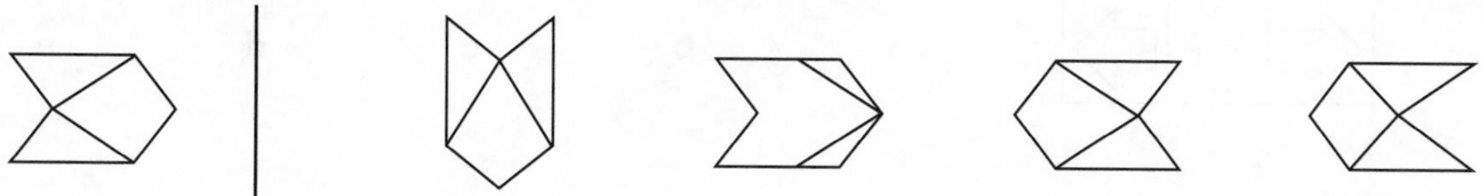

a   b   c   d

Reflect

16.

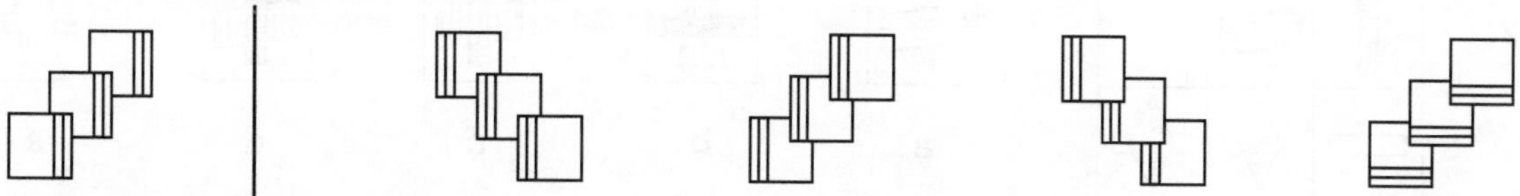

a   b   c   d

Reflect

17.

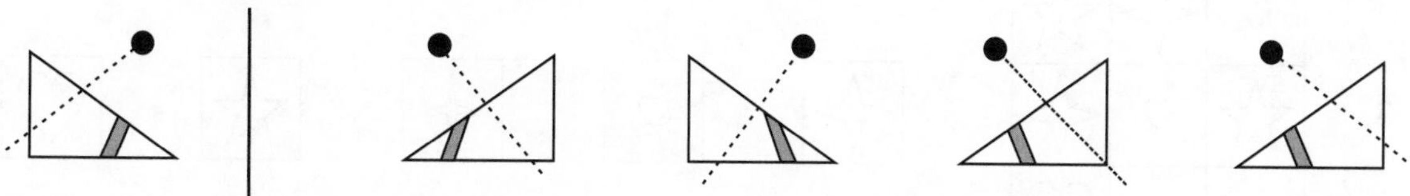

a   b   c   d

Reflect

18.

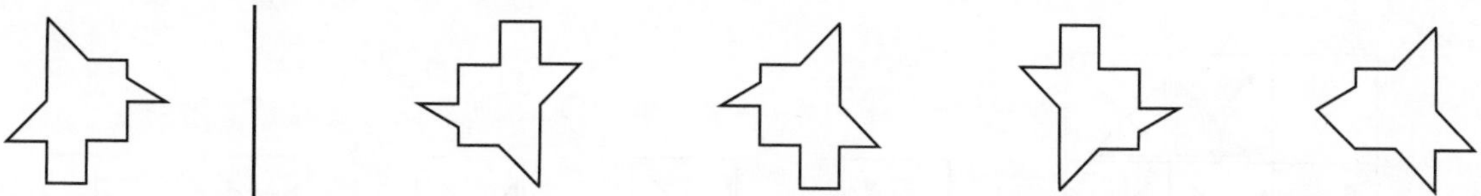

a   b   c   d

/ 18

11

Test 2

You have **10 minutes** to do this test. Circle the letter for each correct answer.

Work out which of the options best fits in place of the missing square in the grid.

1.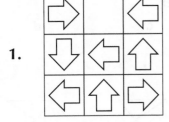

a   b   c   d   e

2.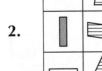

a   b   c   d   e

3.

a   b   c   d   e

4.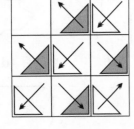

a   b   c   d   e

Test 2   12   © CGP — not to be photocopied

Work out which option would look like the figure on the left if it was rotated.

5.  **Rotate**

    a b c d

6. 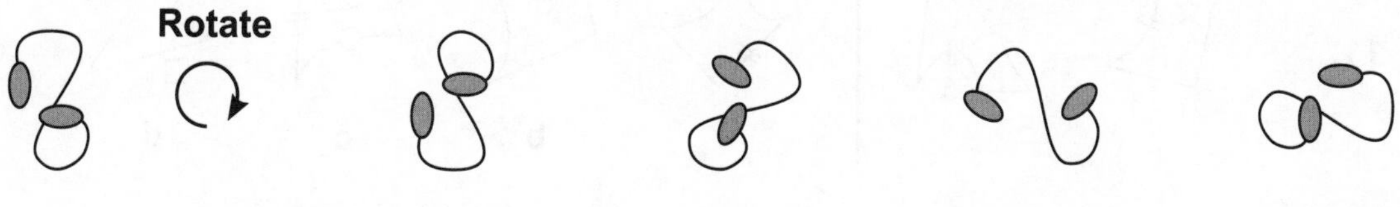   **Rotate**

    a b c d

7.   **Rotate**

    a b c d

8.   **Rotate**

    a b c d

9.   **Rotate** a b c d

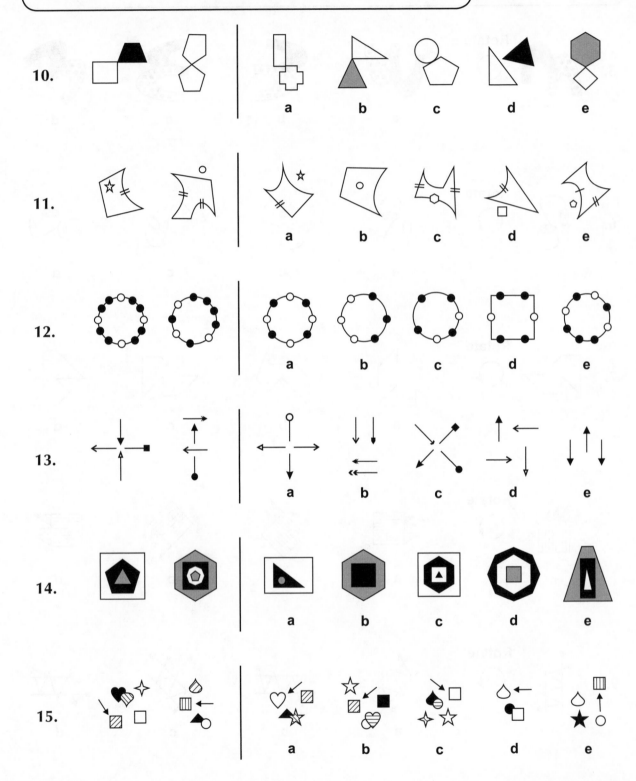

10.   a   b   c   d   e

11.   a   b   c   d   e

12.   a   b   c   d   e

13.   a   b   c   d   e

14.   a   b   c   d   e

15.   a   b   c   d   e

14

Work out which of the four cubes can be made from the net.

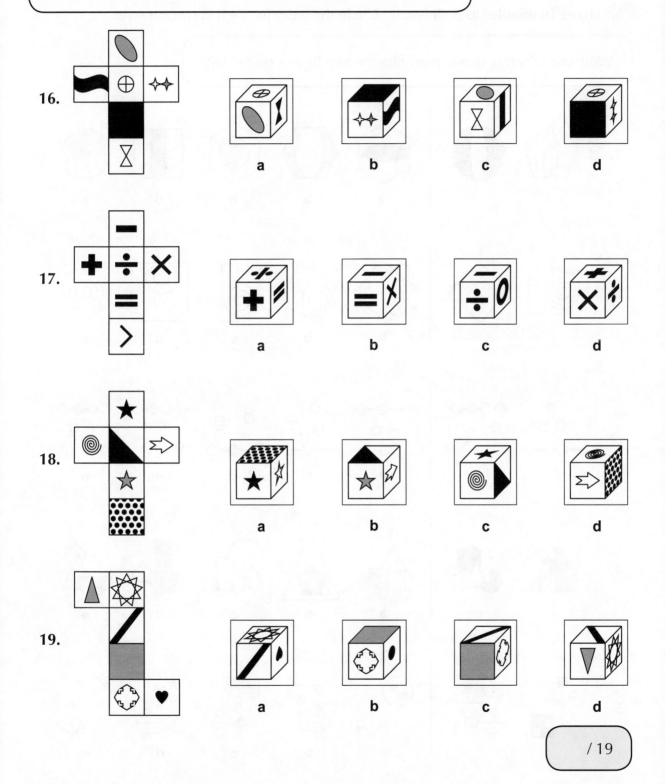

16.   a   b   c   d

17.   a   b   c   d

18.   a   b   c   d

19.   a   b   c   d

/ 19

15

You have **10 minutes** to do this test. Circle the letter for each correct answer.

Work out which option is most like the two figures on the left.

1. |

            a   b   c   d   e

2. |

            a   b   c   d   e

3. |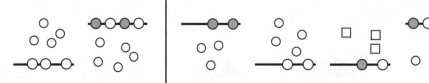

            a   b   c   d   e

4. |

            a   b   c   d   e

5. |

            a   b   c   d   e

Look at how the first bug changes to become the second bug. Then work out which option would look like the third bug if you changed it in the same way.

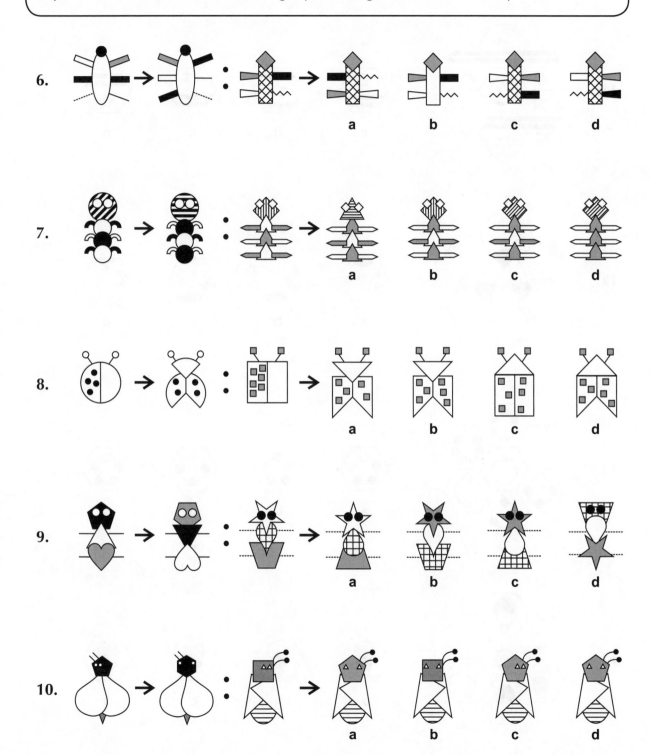

6.

a   b   c   d

7.

a   b   c   d

8.

a   b   c   d

9.

a   b   c   d

10.

a   b   c   d

17

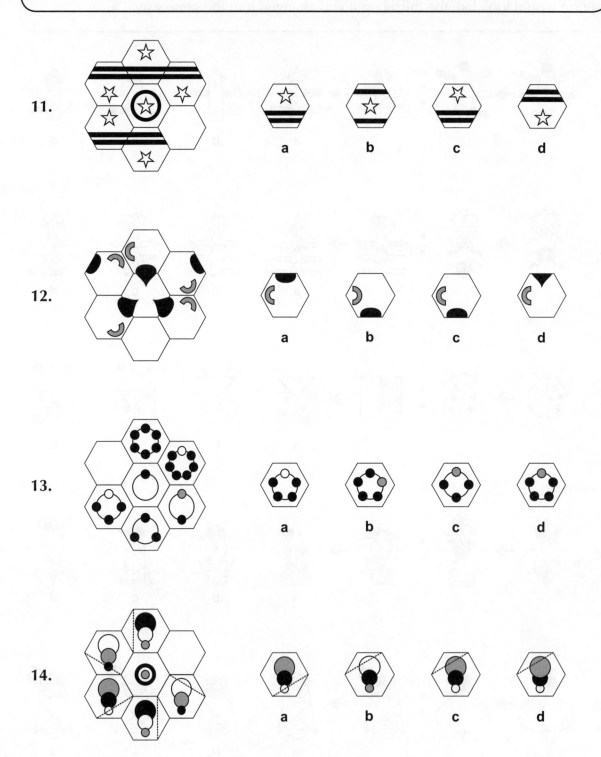

11.

a   b   c   d

12.

a   b   c   d

13.

a   b   c   d

14.

a   b   c   d

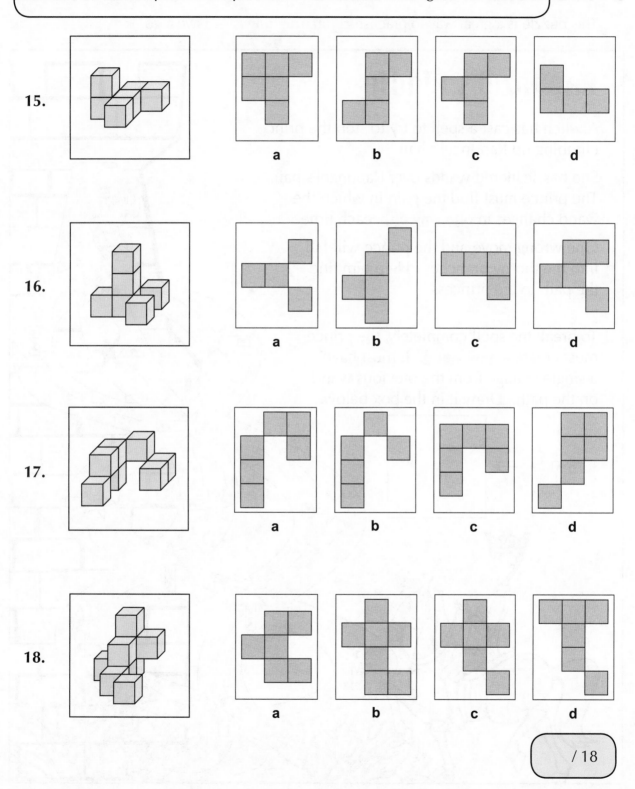

15.

   a   b   c   d

16.

   a   b   c   d

17.

   a   b   c   d

18.

   a   b   c   d

/ 18

Test 3

This puzzle is a great way to practise **comparing things** — have a go.

Rapunzel's Riddle

A witch has cast a spell to try to stop the prince climbing up Rapunzel's hair.

She has scattered wands over Rapunzel's hair. The prince must find the path in which the wand changes in <u>one way only</u> each time.

One wrong move and the prince will fall into the thorny branches. Help him find the path to the princess.

To break the spell completely, the prince must create a <u>new wand</u>. It must have a single change from the previous wand on the path. Draw it in the box below.

You have **10 minutes** to do this test. Circle the letter for each correct answer.

Work out which set of blocks can be put together to make the 3D figure on the left.

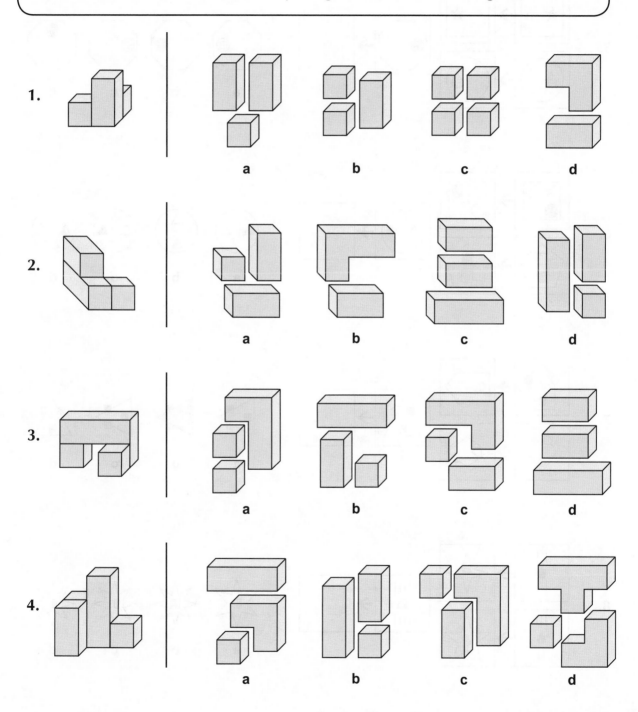

1.

    a   b   c   d

2.

    a   b   c   d

3.

    a   b   c   d

4.

    a   b   c   d

Look at how the first two figures are changed, and then work out which option would look like the third figure if you changed it in the same way.

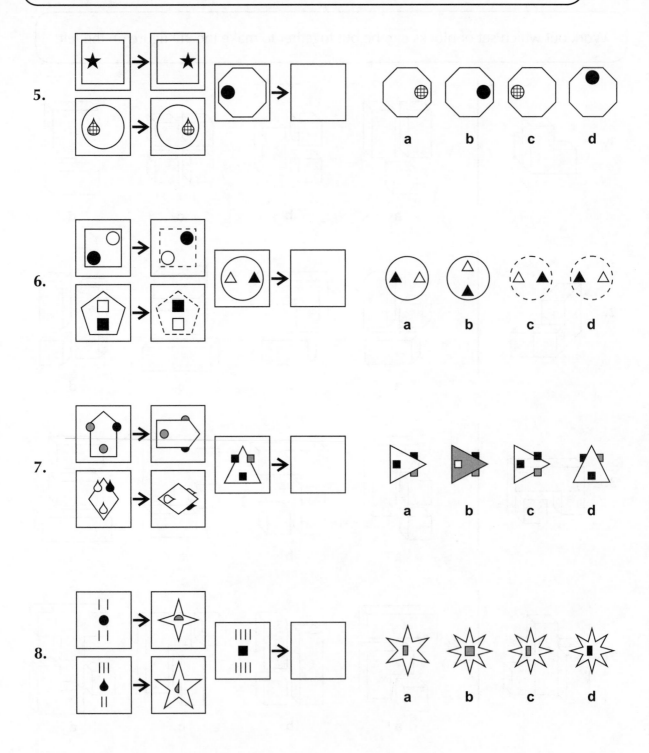

5.

a b c d

6.

a b c d

7.

a b c d

8.

a b c d

22

Work out which option would look like the figure on the left if it was rotated.

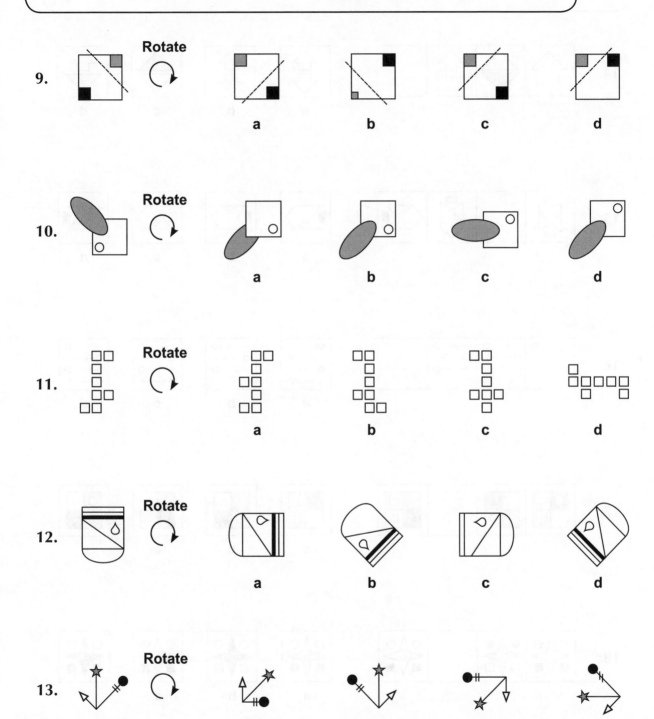

9.

Rotate

a   b   c   d

10.

Rotate

a   b   c   d

11.

Rotate

a   b   c   d

12.

Rotate

a   b   c   d

13.

Rotate

a   b   c   d

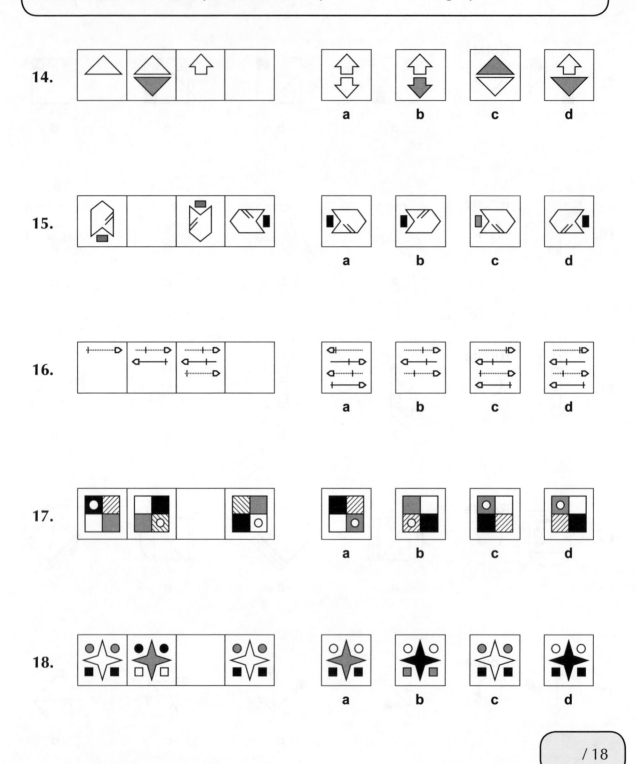

14.

a   b   c   d

15.

a   b   c   d

16.

a   b   c   d

17.

a   b   c   d

18.

a   b   c   d

/ 18

You have **10 minutes** to do this test. Circle the letter for each correct answer.

Work out which option would look like the figure on the left if it was reflected over the line.

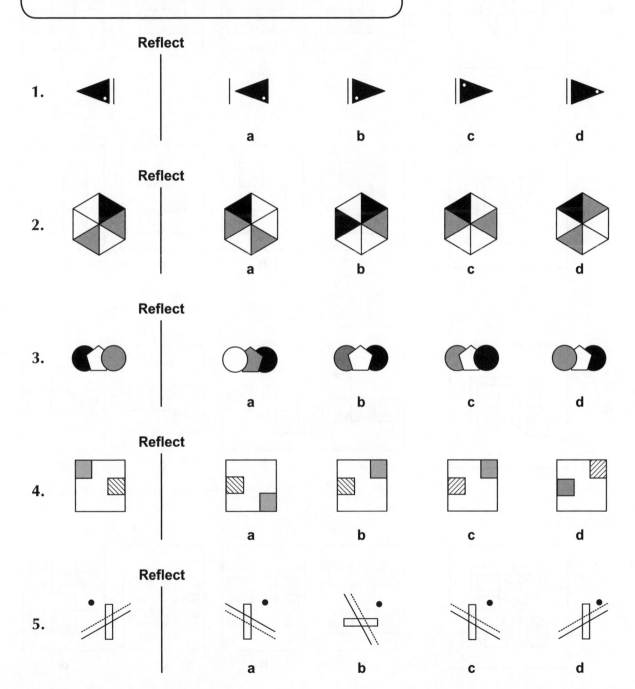

Work out which option is a top-down 2D view of the 3D figure on the left.

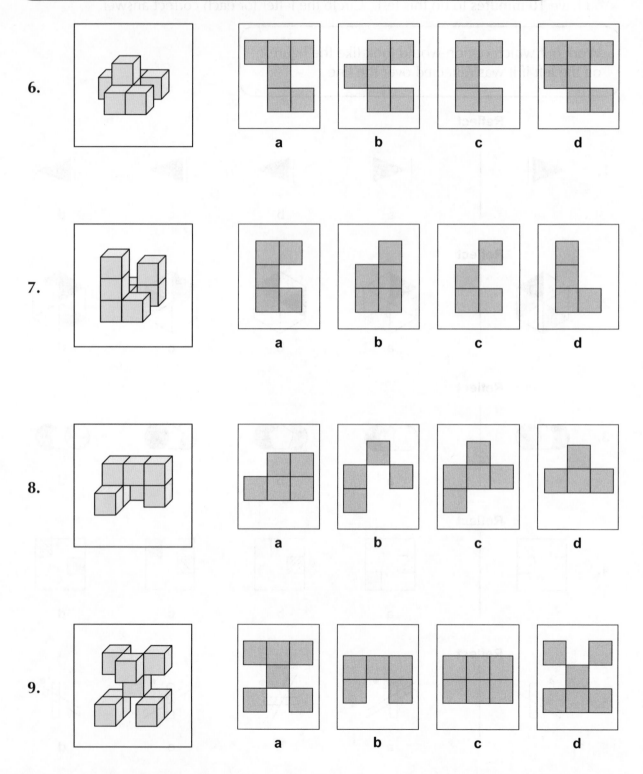

6.

a   b   c   d

7.

a   b   c   d

8.

a   b   c   d

9.

a   b   c   d

10.

11.

12.

13.

14.

15.

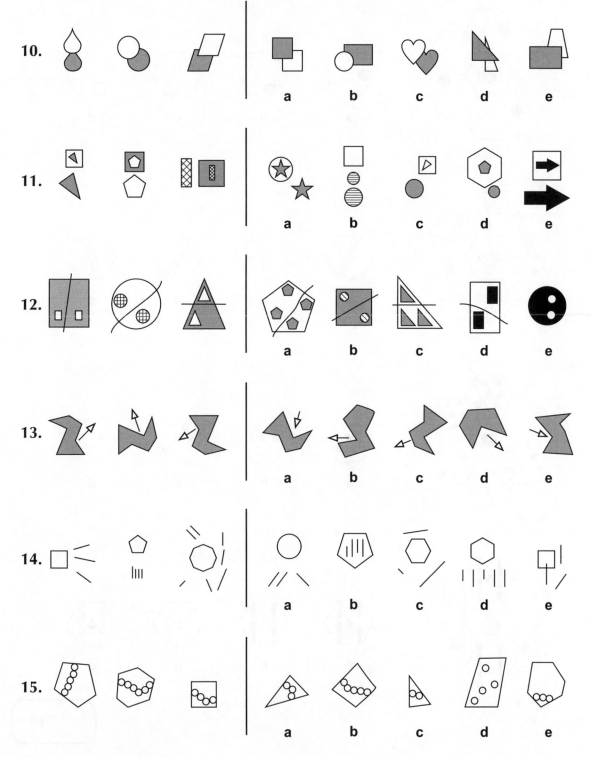

a   b   c   d   e

27

Work out which of the options best fits in place of the missing hexagon in the grid.

16.

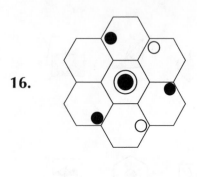

a   b   c   d

17.

a   b   c   d

18.

a   b   c   d

19.

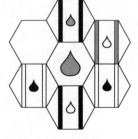

a   b   c   d

/ 19

You have **10 minutes** to do this test. Circle the letter for each correct answer.

Work out which option is most like the three figures on the left.

1.

                                                a   b   c   d   e

2.

                                                a   b   c   d   e

3.

                                                a   b   c   d   e

4.

                                                a   b   c   d   e

5.

                                                a   b   c   d   e

Work out which option would look like the figure
on the left if it was reflected over the line.

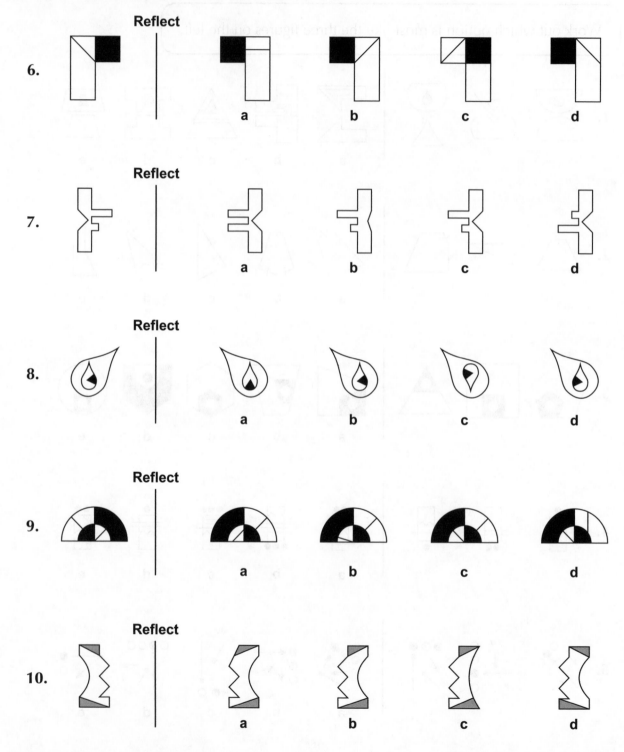

Reflect

6.

a   b   c   d

Reflect

7.

a   b   c   d

Reflect

8.

a   b   c   d

Reflect

9.

a   b   c   d

Reflect

10.

a   b   c   d

30

Find the figure in each row that is most unlike the others.

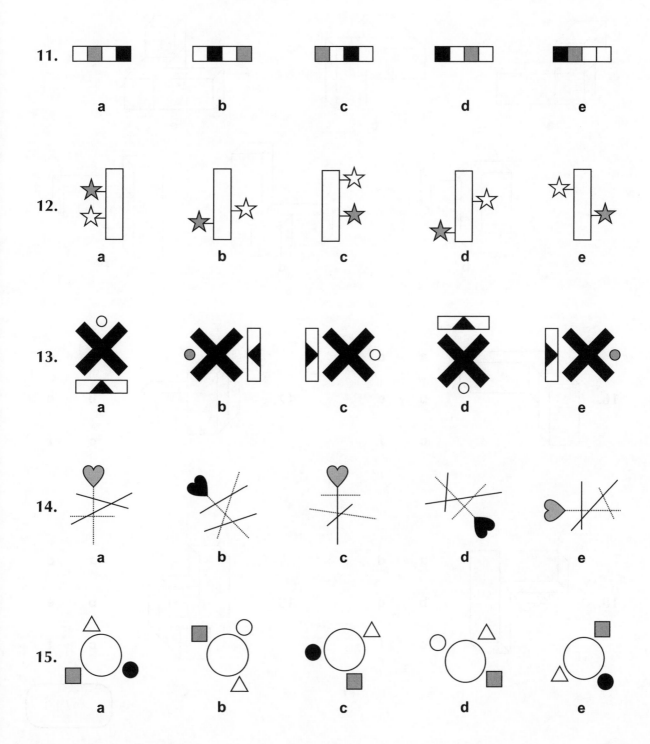

31

Work out which 3D figure in the grey box has been rotated to make the new 3D figure.

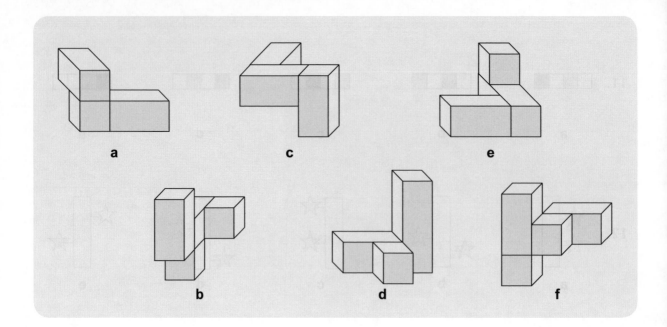

a

c

e

b

d

f

16.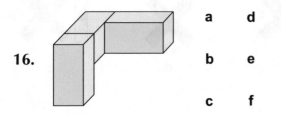

a   d

b   e

c   f

17.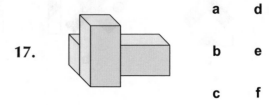

a   d

b   e

c   f

18.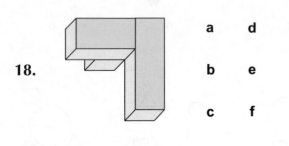

a   d

b   e

c   f

19.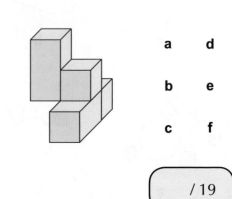

a   d

b   e

c   f

/ 19

Time for some puzzles. They're a great way to practise your skills a bit more.

Snakes and Ladders

The snakes and ladders board below has six missing squares.
The spaces are marked with a letter.
Write the letter of the space where each square should go.

1 = _   2 = _   3 = _

4 = _   5 = _   6 = _

Unlock the Treasure

Percy the pirate has dug up a treasure chest and six keys.
Which key will unlock the chest?

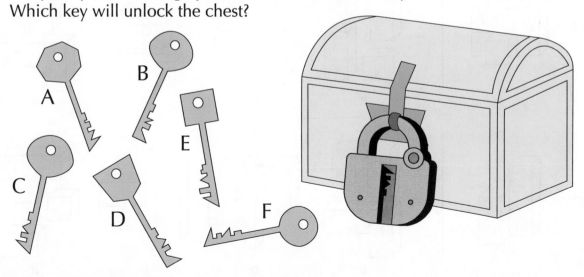

33

You have **10 minutes** to do this test. Circle the letter for each correct answer.

Work out which set of blocks can be put together to make the 3D figure on the left.

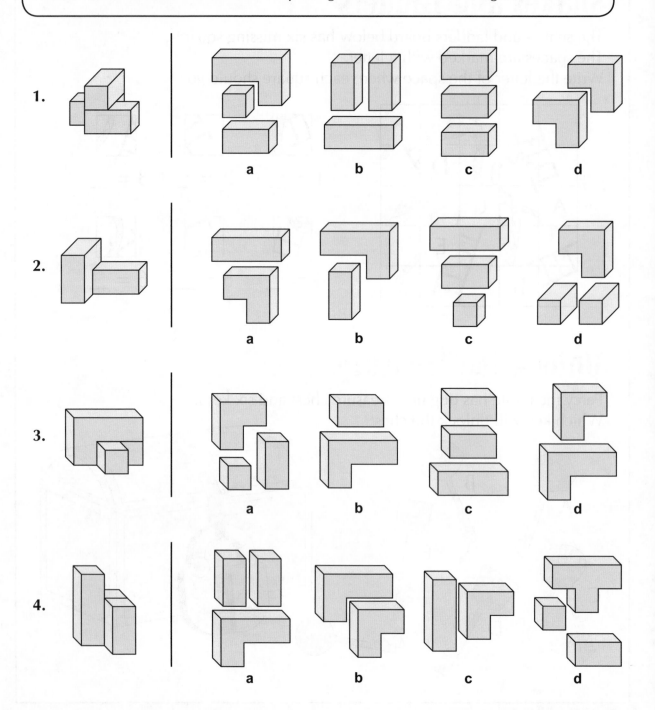

1.

    a   b   c   d

2.

    a   b   c   d

3.

    a   b   c   d

4.

    a   b   c   d

Work out which option would look like the figure on the left if it was rotated.

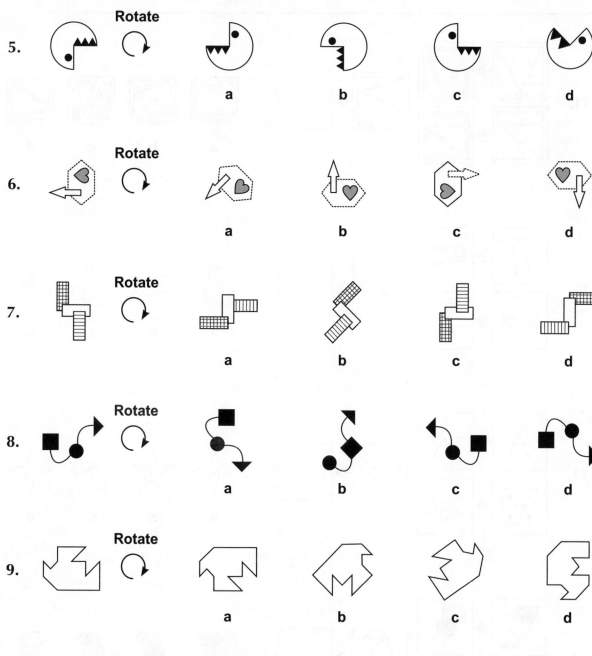

5. Rotate

    a   b   c   d

6. Rotate

    a   b   c   d

7. Rotate

    a   b   c   d

8. Rotate

    a   b   c   d

9. Rotate

    a   b   c   d

10. Rotate

    a   b   c   d

Look at how the first two figures are changed, and then work out which option would look like the third figure if you changed it in the same way.

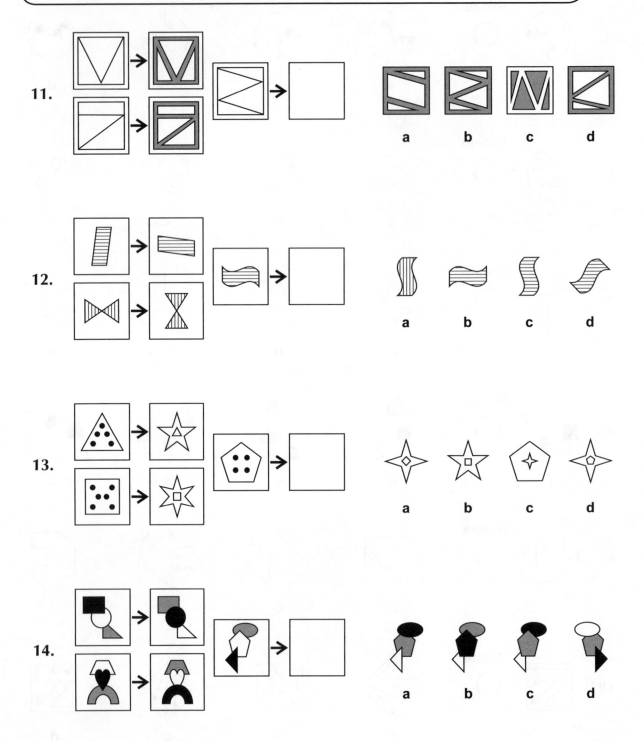

11.

12.

13.

14.

a   b   c   d

Work out which of the options best fits in place of the missing square in the grid.

15.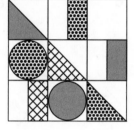

a   b   c   d   e

16.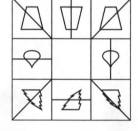

a   b   c   d   e

17.

a   b   c   d   e

18.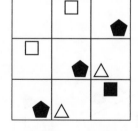

a   b   c   d   e

/ 18

Test 7

You have **10 minutes** to do this test. Circle the letter for each correct answer.

Find the figure in each row that is most unlike the others.

1.

     a   b   c   d   e

2.

     a   b   c   d   e

3.

     a   b   c   d   e

4.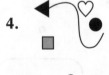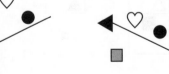

     a   b   c   d   e

Work out which of the options best fits in place of the missing hexagon in the grid.

5.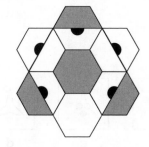

            a   **b**   **c**   **d**

6.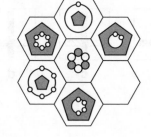

            a   **b**   **c**   **d**

7.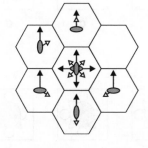

            a   **b**   **c**   **d**

8.

            a   **b**   **c**   **d**

Test 8

Work out which of the options best fits in place of the missing square in the series.

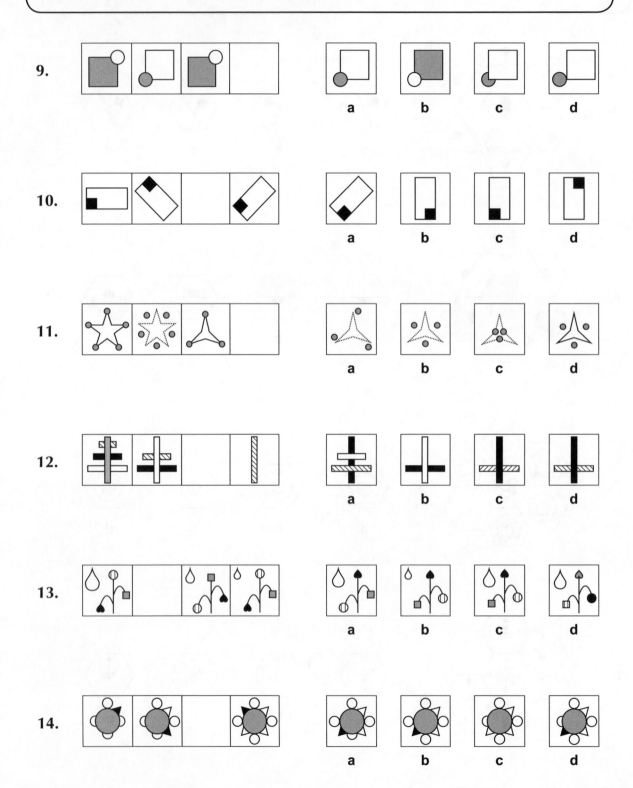

9.

a   b   c   d

10.

a   b   c   d

11.

a   b   c   d

12.

a   b   c   d

13.

a   b   c   d

14.

a   b   c   d

40

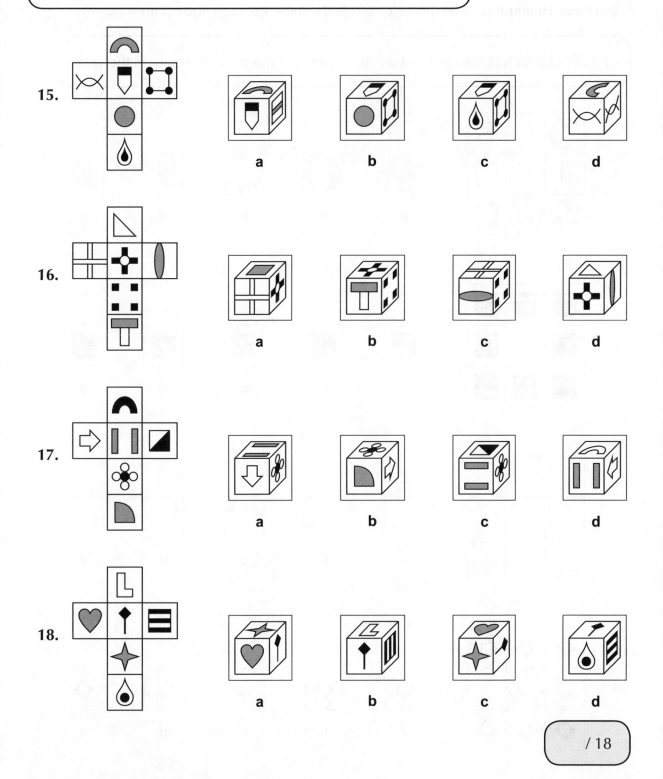

15.　　a　　b　　c　　d

16.　　a　　b　　c　　d

17.　　a　　b　　c　　d

18.　　a　　b　　c　　d

/ 18

Test 8

You have **10 minutes** to do this test. Circle the letter for each correct answer.

Work out which of the options best fits in place of the missing square in the grid.

1.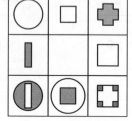

    a   b   c   d   e

2.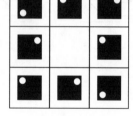

    a   b   c   d   e

3.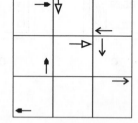

    a   b   c   d   e

4.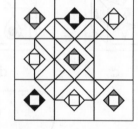

    a   b   c   d   e

Work out which option would look like the figure on the left if it was reflected over the line.

Reflect

5.

      a   b   c   d

Reflect

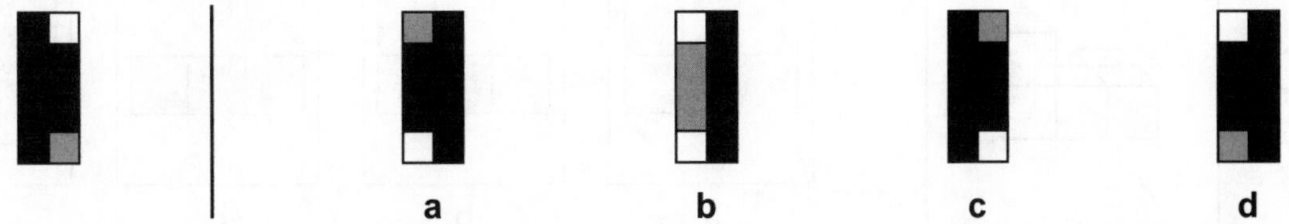

6.

      a   b   c   d

Reflect

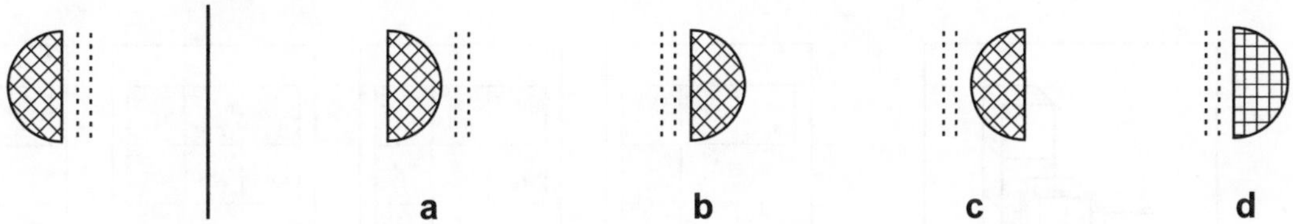

7.

      a   b   c   d

Reflect

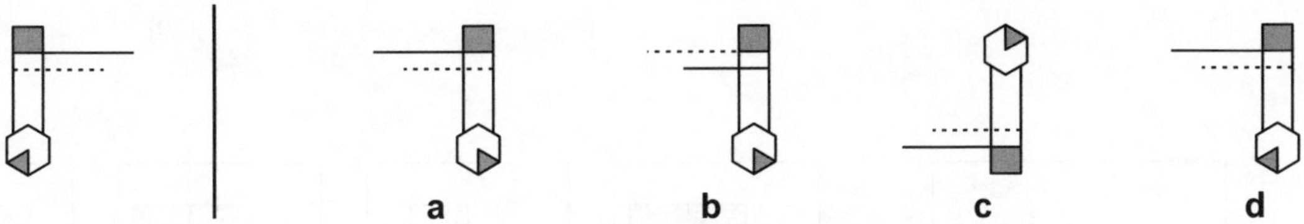

8.

      a   b   c   d

Reflect

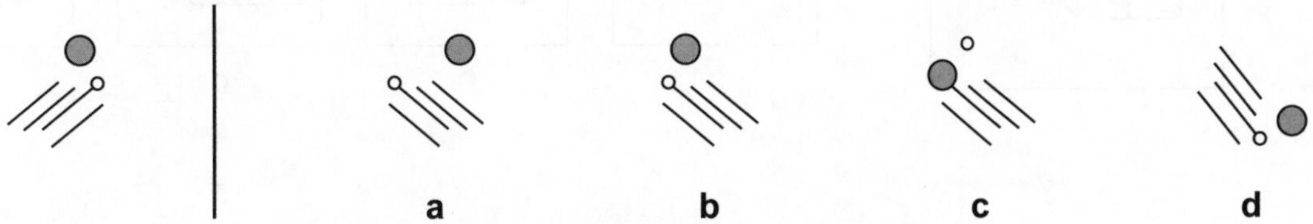

9.

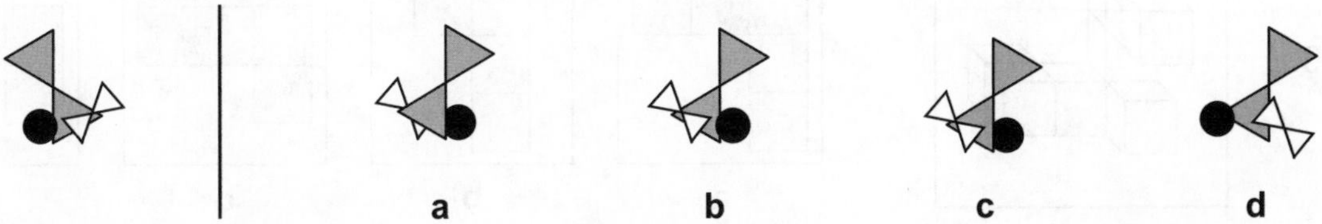

      a   b   c   d

Work out which option is a top-down 2D view of the 3D figure on the left.

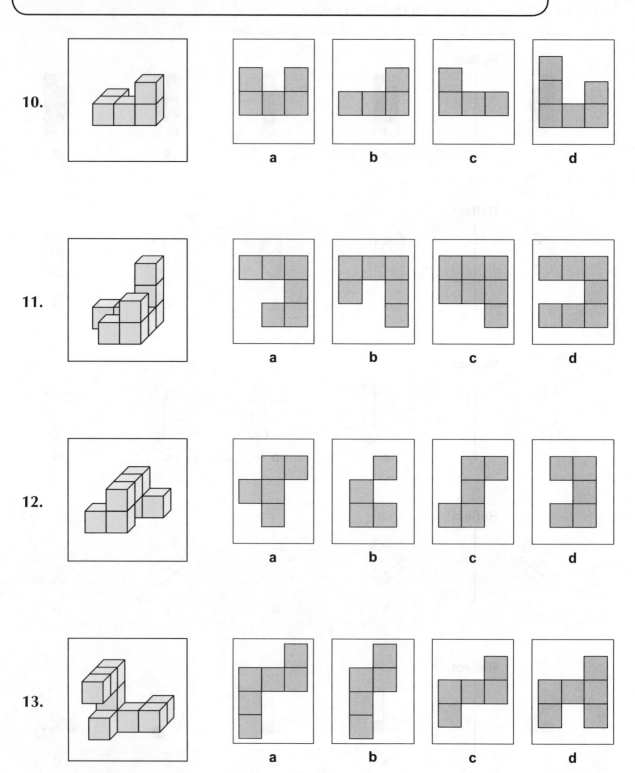

10.

    a   b   c   d

11.

    a   b   c   d

12.

    a   b   c   d

13.

    a   b   c   d

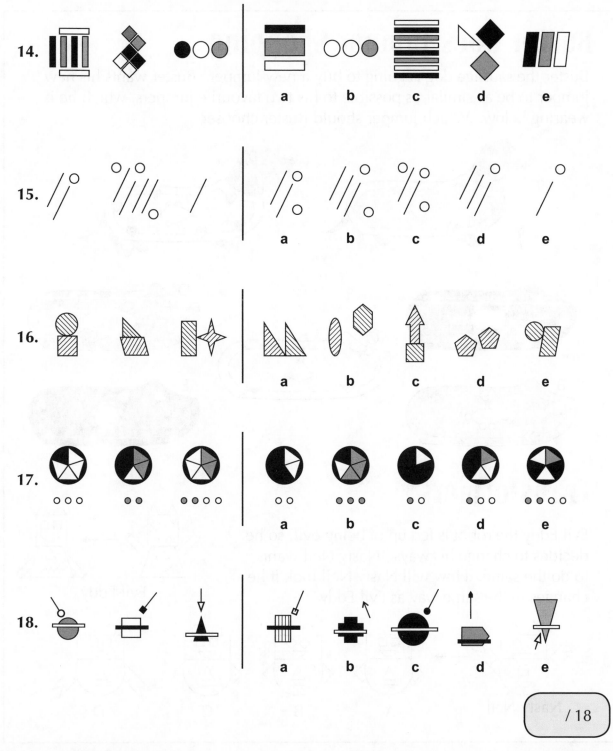

14.   a   b   c   d   e

15.   a   b   c   d   e

16.   a   b   c   d   e

17.   a   b   c   d   e

18.   a   b   c   d   e

/ 18

These puzzles will help you **spot connections** between figures — so give them a go.

Buster Goes Jumper Shopping

Buster the sausage dog is going to buy a new jumper. Buster wants his new jumper to be as similar as possible to his two favourite jumpers, which he is wearing below. Which jumper should Buster choose?

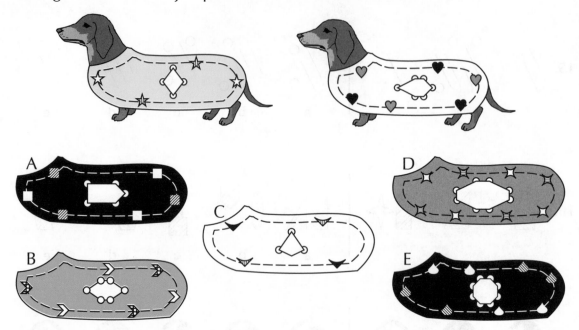

Transformers

Evil Eddy the robot is fed up of being evil, so he decides to change his ways. Nasty Neil wants to do the same. How will Nasty Neil look if he changes in the same way as Evil Eddy?

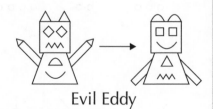

Evil Eddy

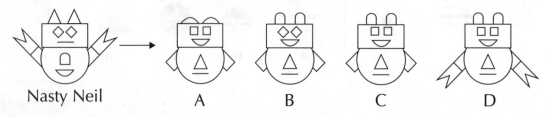

Nasty Neil A B C D

46

You have **10 minutes** to do this test. Circle the letter for each correct answer.

> Work out which option is most like the two figures on the left.

1. |

a   b   c   d   e

2. |

a   b   c   d   e

3. |

a   b   c   d   e

4. |

a   b   c   d   e

5. |

a   b   c   d   e

Work out which 3D figure in the grey box has been rotated to make the new 3D figure.

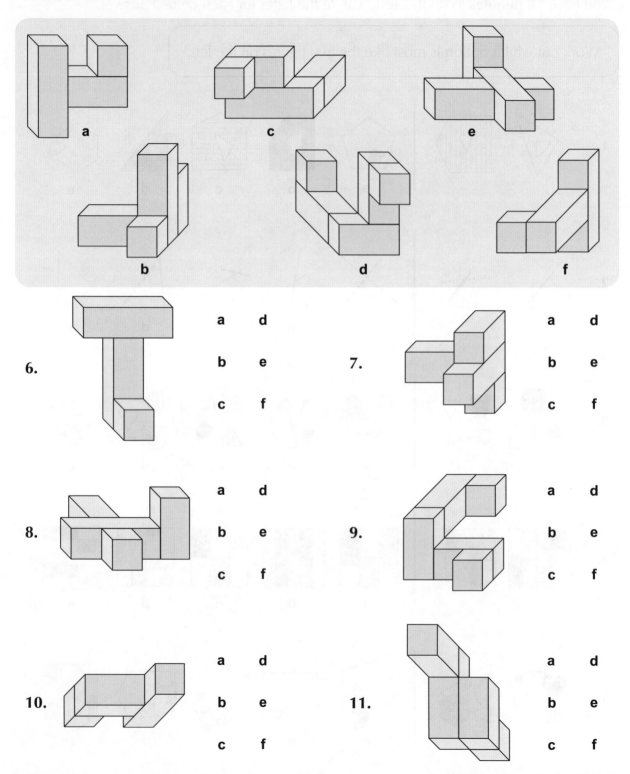

a

b

c

d

e

f

6.

a   d

b   e

c   f

7.

a   d

b   e

c   f

8.

a   d

b   e

c   f

9.

a   d

b   e

c   f

10.

a   d

b   e

c   f

11.

a   d

b   e

c   f

48

Work out which of the options best fits in place of the missing hexagon in the grid.

12.

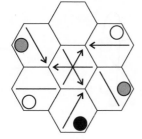

a　　　　b　　　　c　　　　d

13.

a　　　　b　　　　c　　　　d

14.

a　　　　b　　　　c　　　　d

15.

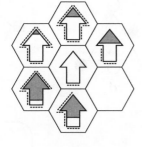

a　　　　b　　　　c　　　　d

Test 10

Find the figure in each row that is most unlike the others.

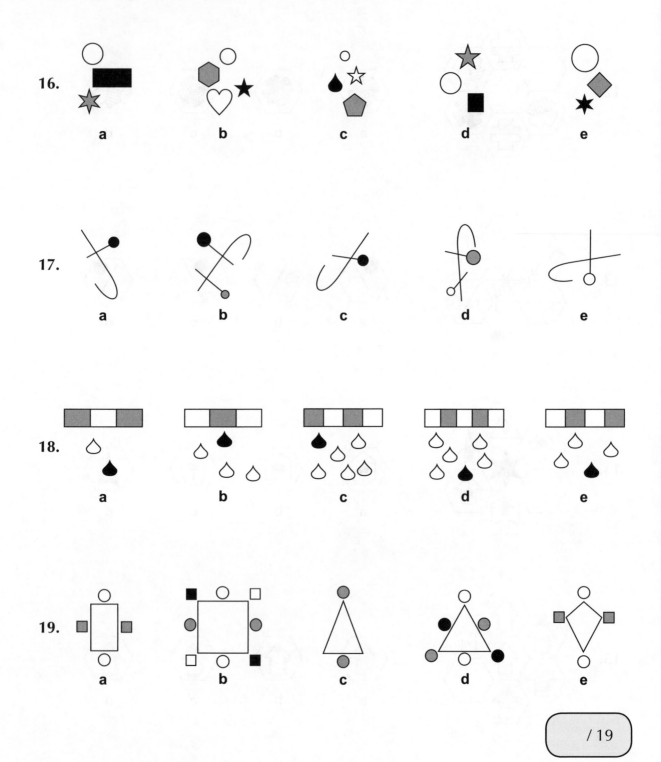

16. a b c d e

17. a b c d e

18. a b c d e

19. a b c d e

/ 19

You have **10 minutes** to do this test. Circle the letter for each correct answer.

> Work out which option is most like the three figures on the left.

1.

a   b   c   d   e

2.

a   b   c   d   e

3.

a   b   c   d   e

4.

a   b   c   d   e

5.

a   b   c   d   e

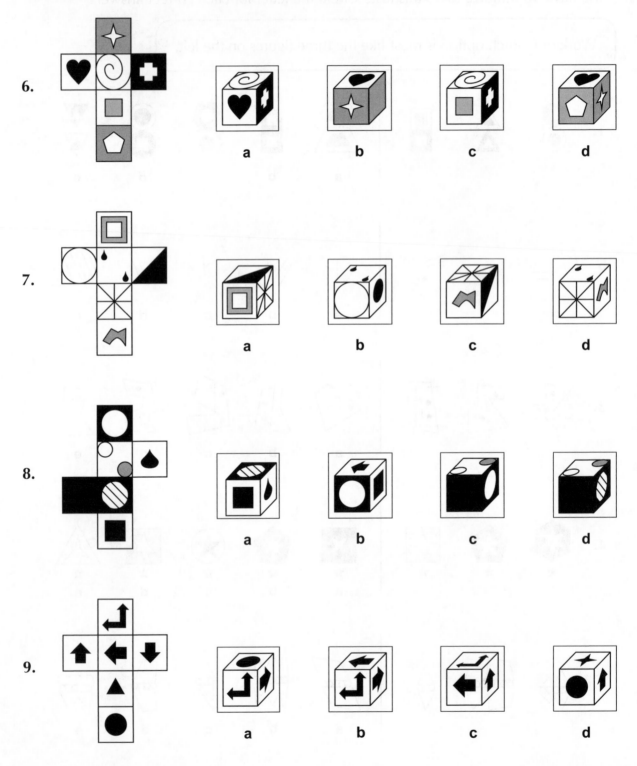

6.

a   b   c   d

7.

a   b   c   d

8.

a   b   c   d

9.

a   b   c   d

Look at how the first bug changes to become the second bug. Then work out which option would look like the third bug if you changed it in the same way.

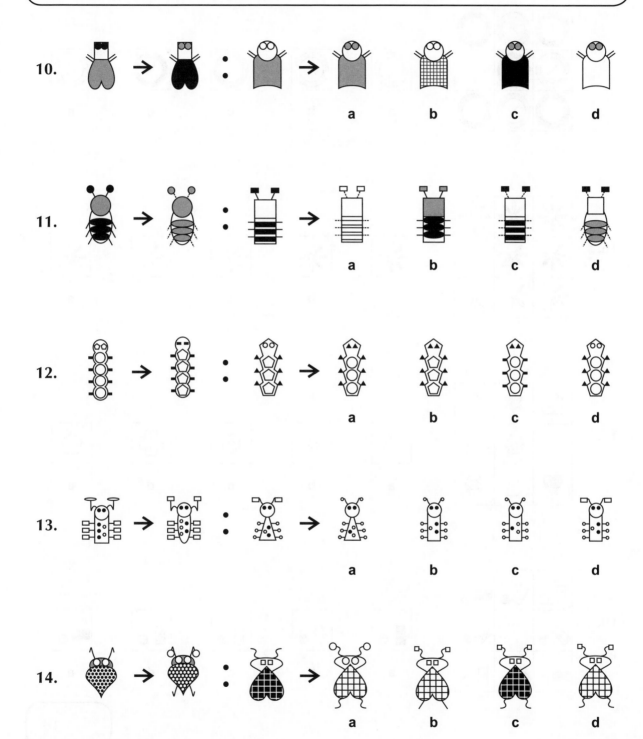

10.

a   b   c   d

11.

a   b   c   d

12.

a   b   c   d

13.

a   b   c   d

14.

a   b   c   d

53

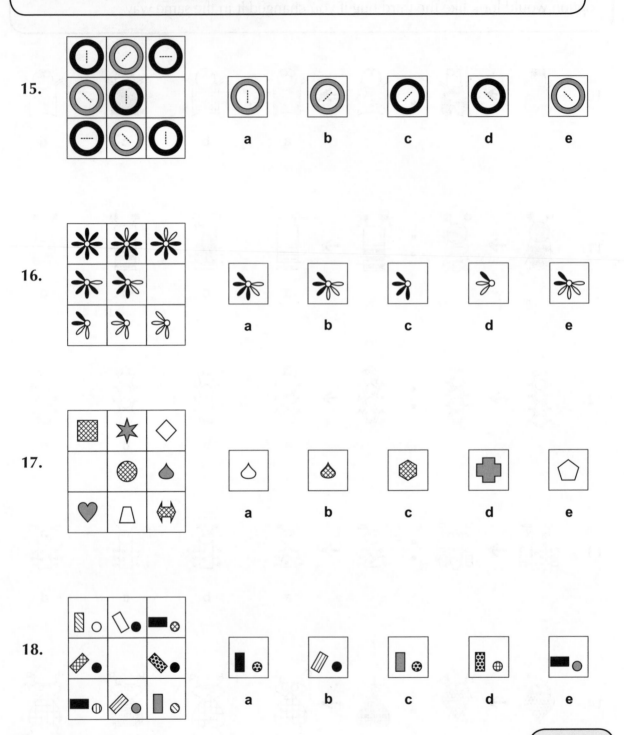

15.

a   b   c   d   e

16.

a   b   c   d   e

17.

a   b   c   d   e

18.

a   b   c   d   e

/ 18

Test 12

You have **10 minutes** to do this test. Circle the letter for each correct answer.

Work out which option would look like the figure on the left if it was rotated.

1. 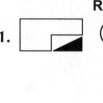 **Rotate**

              a   **b**   **c**   **d**

2. **Rotate**

              a   **b**   **c**   **d**

3. **Rotate**

              a   **b**   **c**   **d**

4.  **Rotate**

              a   **b**   **c**   **d**

5. **Rotate**

              a   **b**   **c**   **d**

Work out which option is a top-down 2D view of the 3D figure on the left.

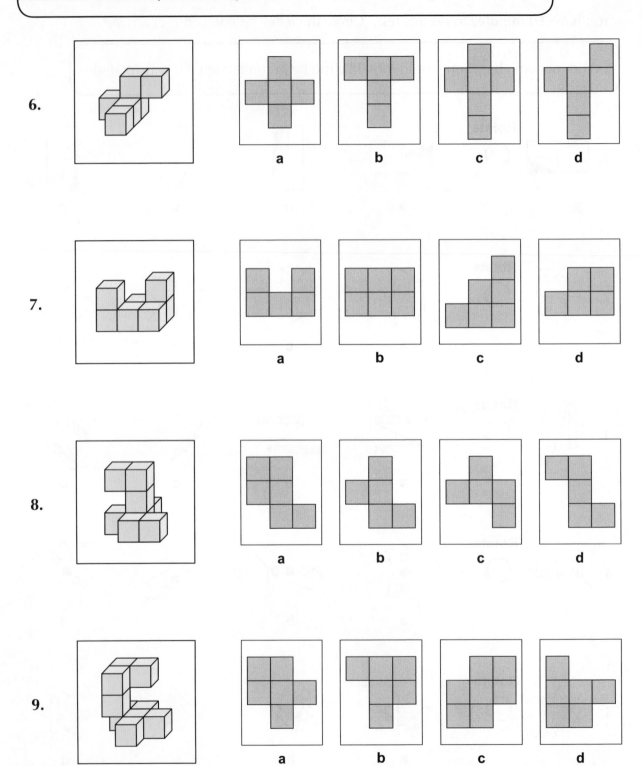

6.

a

b

c

d

7.

a

b

c

d

8.

a

b

c

d

9.

a

b

c

d

Work out which of the options best fits in place of the missing square in the series.

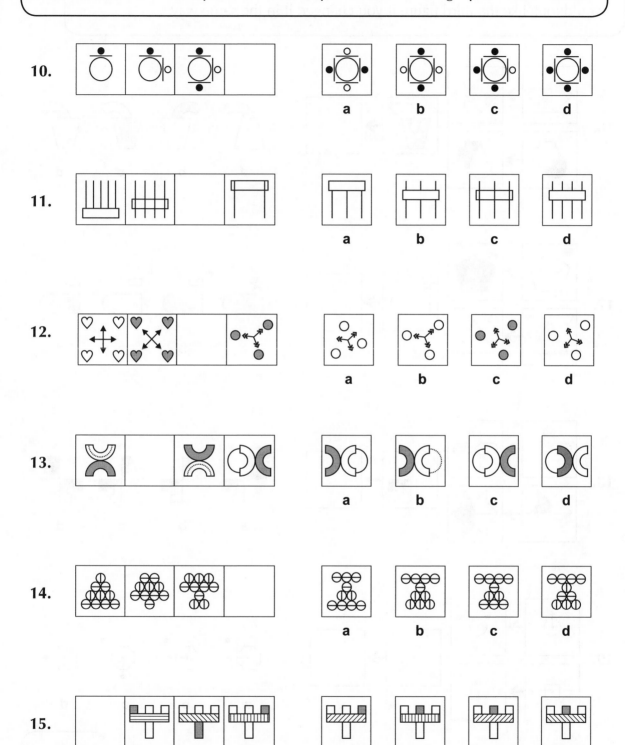

10.

                      a   b   c   d

11.

                      a   b   c   d

12.

                      a   b   c   d

13.

                      a   b   c   d

14.

                      a   b   c   d

15.

                      a   b   c   d

Look at how the first two figures are changed, and then work out which option would look like the third figure if you changed it in the same way.

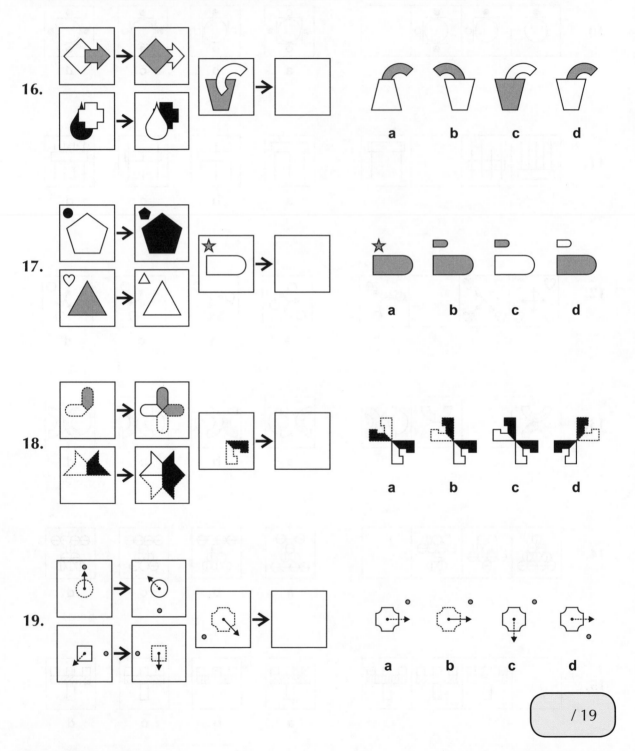

16.

a   b   c   d

17.

a   b   c   d

18.

a   b   c   d

19.

a   b   c   d

/ 19

Now it's time for some puzzles! They're a brilliant way to practise your skills.

Judging Giraffes

Geoffrey and Gerald Giraffe are auditioning for a third member
to join their band. The new member must share their look.
Circle the giraffe that they should choose.

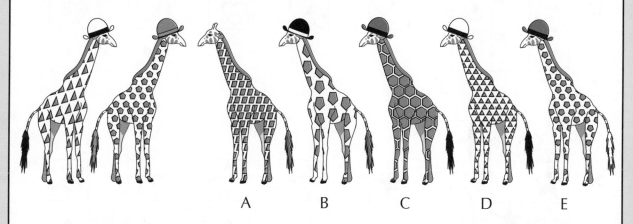

A   B   C   D   E

Runaway Train

A train has lost one of its carriages. All of its carriages follow a sequence.
Circle the carriage that belongs at the end of the train.

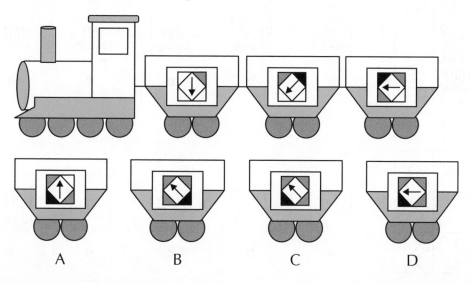

A   B   C   D

You have **10 minutes** to do this test. Circle the letter for each correct answer.

Work out which of the options best fits in place of the missing square in the grid.

1.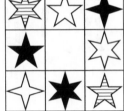

a   b   c   d   e

2.

a   b   c   d   e

3.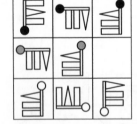

a   b   c   d   e

4.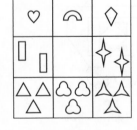

a   b   c   d   e

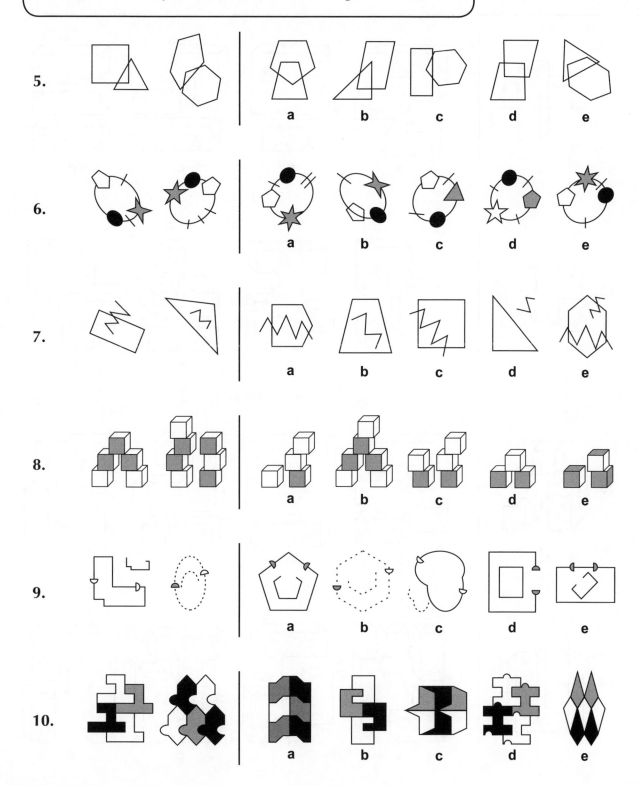

5.

a   b   c   d   e

6.

a   b   c   d   e

7.

a   b   c   d   e

8.

a   b   c   d   e

9.

a   b   c   d   e

10.

a   b   c   d   e

61

Work out which set of blocks can be put together to make the 3D figure on the left.

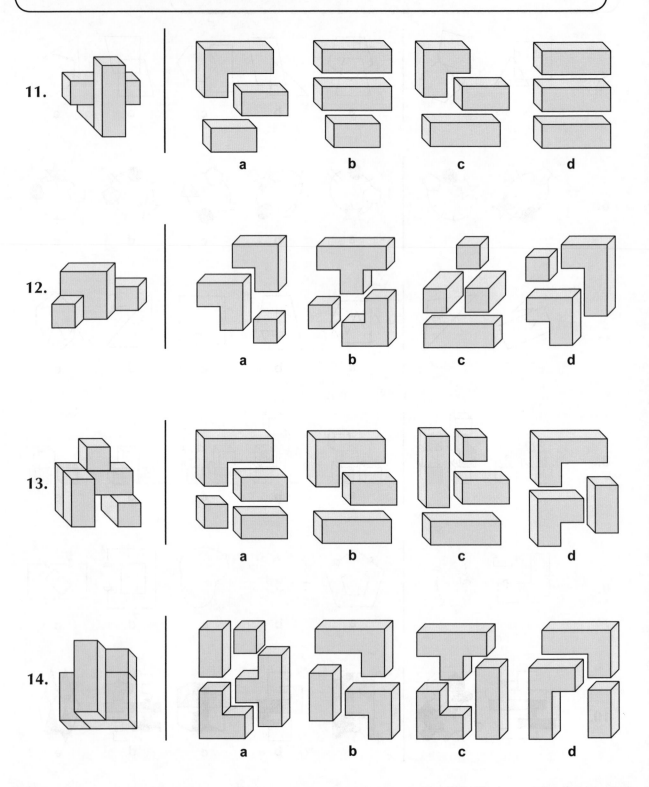

11.   a   b   c   d

12.   a   b   c   d

13.   a   b   c   d

14.   a   b   c   d

Find the figure in each row that is most unlike the others.

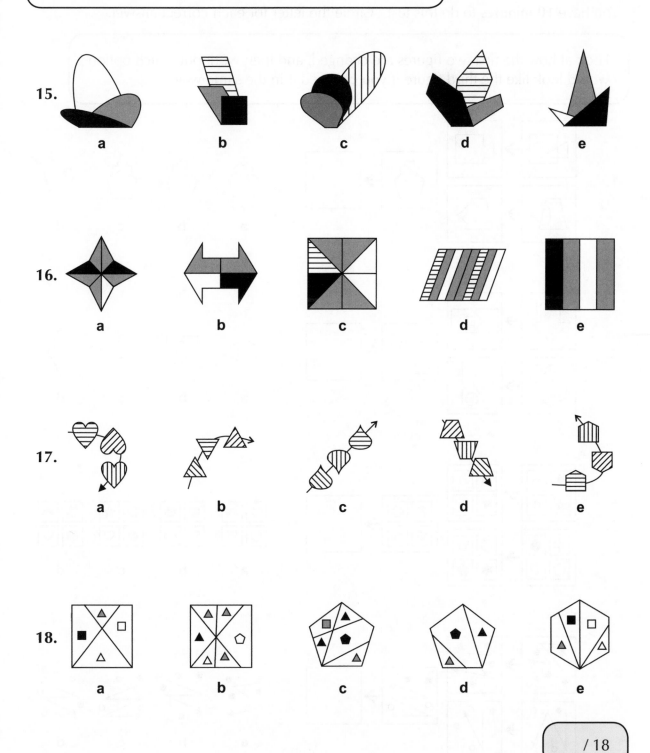

15.

    a   b   c   d   e

16.

    a   b   c   d   e

17.

    a   b   c   d   e

18.

    a   b   c   d   e

/ 18

Test 13

You have **10 minutes** to do this test. Circle the letter for each correct answer.

> Look at how the first two figures are changed, and then work out which option
> would look like the third figure if you changed it in the same way.

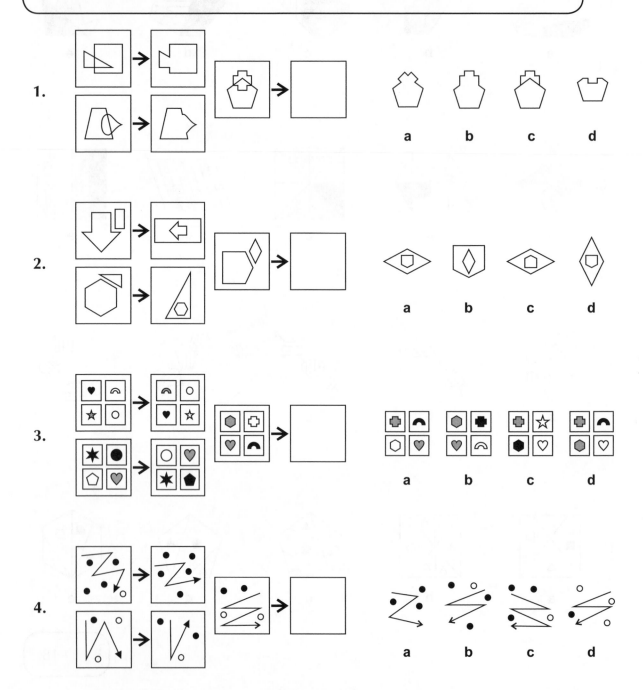

1.

a   b   c   d

2.

a   b   c   d

3.

a   b   c   d

4.

a   b   c   d

Work out which option would look like the figure on the left if it was reflected over the line.

Reflect

5.
 a
 b
 c
 d

Reflect

6.
 a
 b
 c
 d

Reflect

7.
 a
 b
 c
 d

Reflect

8.
 a
 b
 c
 d

Reflect

9.
 a   
 b
 c   d

65

Work out which 3D figure in the grey box has been rotated to make the new 3D figure.

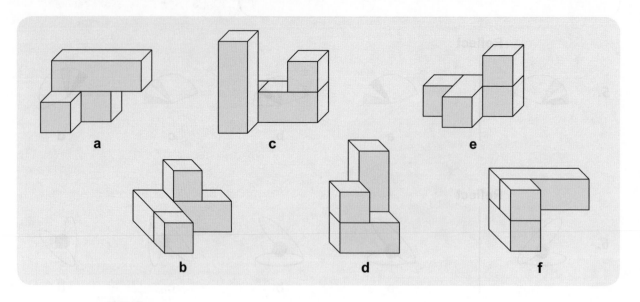

a

c

e

b

d

f

10.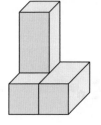

a   d

b   e

c   f

11.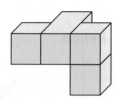

a   d

b   e

c   f

12.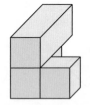

a   d

b   e

c   f

13.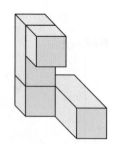

a   d

b   e

c   f

14.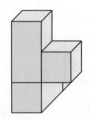

a   d

b   e

c   f

15.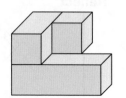

a   d

b   e

c   f

Work out which of the options best fits in place of the missing hexagon in the grid.

16.

a   b   c   d

17.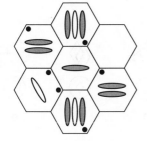

a   b   c   d

18.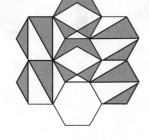

a   b   c   d

19.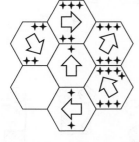

a   b   c   d

/ 19

67

You have **10 minutes** to do this test. Circle the letter for each correct answer.

Work out which option is most like the three figures on the left.

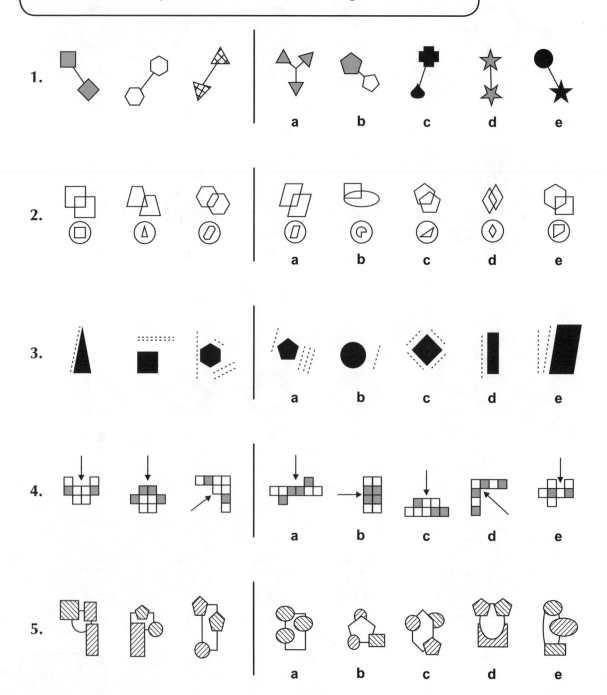

68

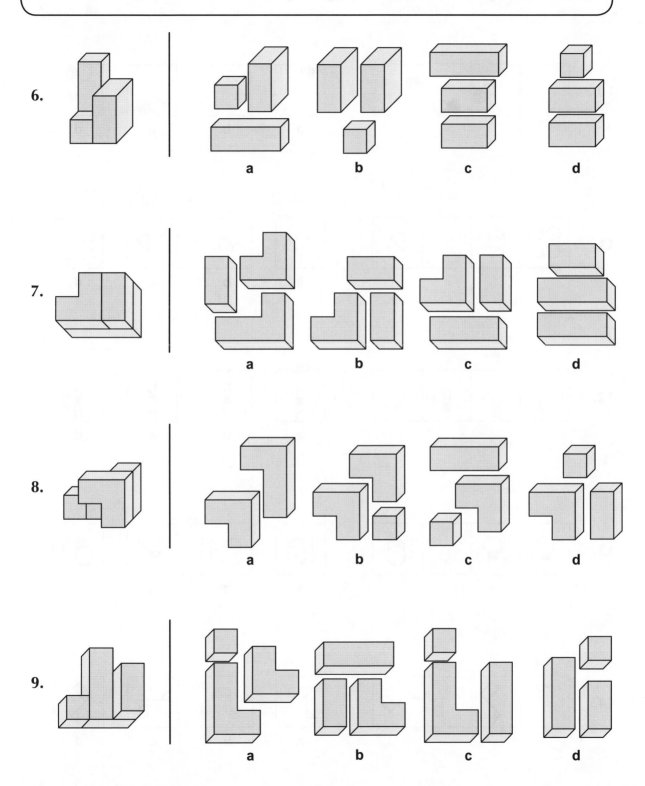

6.

a   b   c   d

7.

a   b   c   d

8.

a   b   c   d

9.

a   b   c   d

Work out which of the options best fits in place of the missing square in the series.

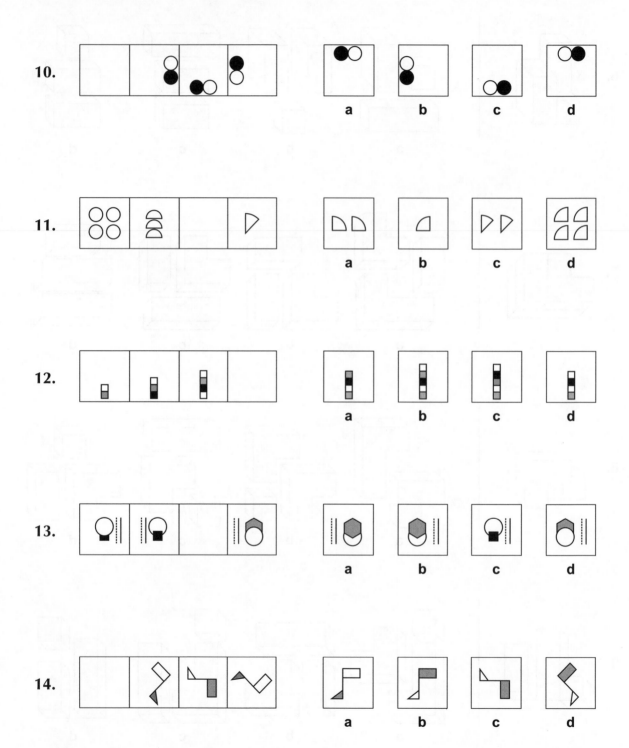

10.

a   b   c   d

11.

a   b   c   d

12.

a   b   c   d

13.

a   b   c   d

14.

a   b   c   d

Find the figure in each row that is most unlike the others.

15.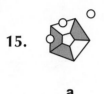

     a   b   c   d   e

16.

     a   b   c   d   e

17.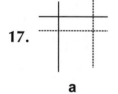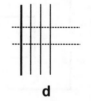

     a   b   c   d   e

18.

     a   b   c   d   e

/ 18

Test 15

You'll need your best pattern-spotting head on to find your way through these puzzles.

Mischievous Maze

Some blocks have been dropped into the maze below.
Draw a line to show the way through the maze.
You can only pass through blocks that follow a sequence.

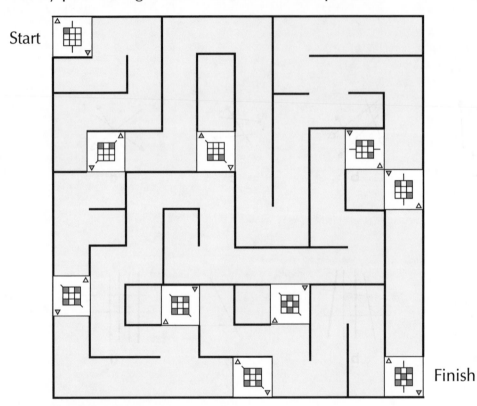

Cecil's New Coat

Cecil has a new patterned coat. Unfortunately the last section is missing.
Draw in the missing section by continuing the sequence.

You have **10 minutes** to do this test. Circle the letter for each correct answer.

Work out which of the options best fits in place of the missing square in the series.

1.

                                                  a   **b**   **c**   **d**

2.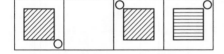

                                                  a   **b**   **c**   **d**

3.

                                                  a   **b**   **c**   **d**

4.

                                                  a   **b**   **c**   **d**

5.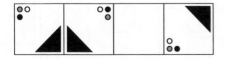

                                                  a   **b**   **c**   **d**

Work out which option is a top-down 2D view of the 3D figure on the left.

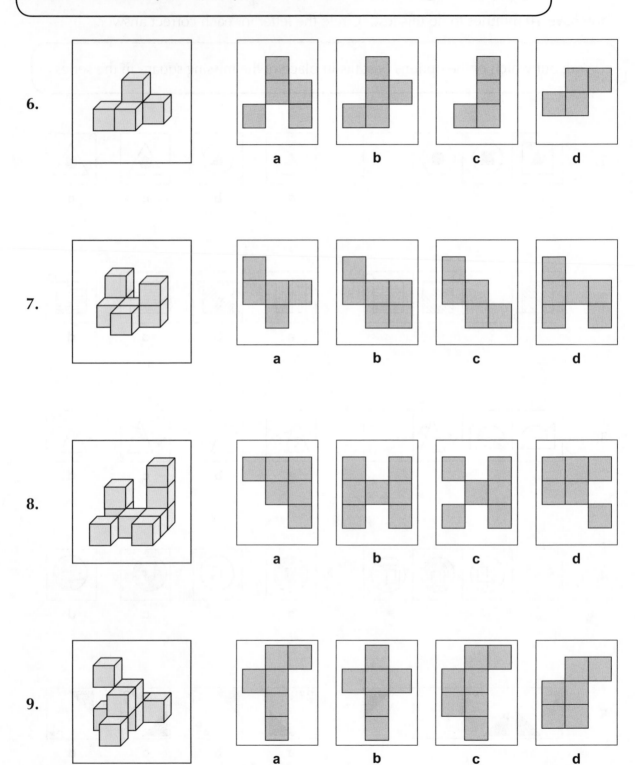

6.
a   b   c   d

7.
a   b   c   d

8.
a   b   c   d

9.
a   b   c   d

Work out which option would look like the figure on the left if it was rotated.

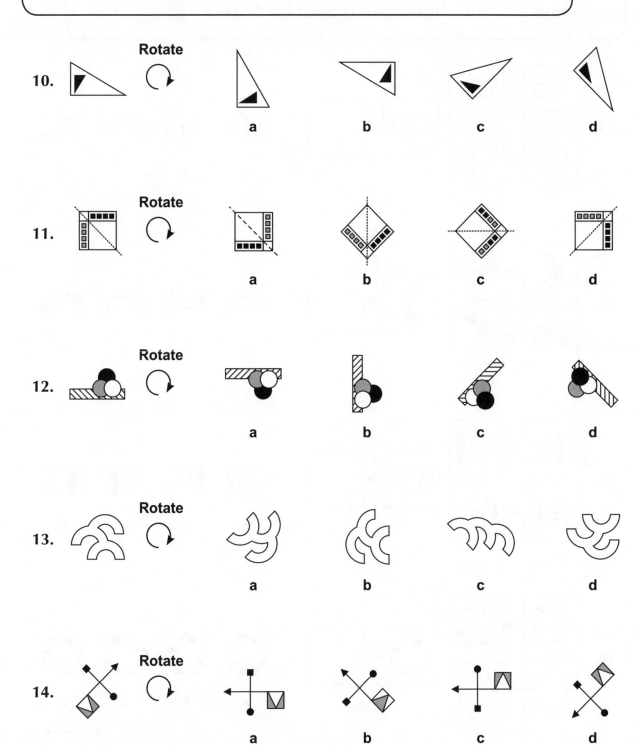

10. Rotate

a   b   c   d

11. Rotate

a   b   c   d

12. Rotate

a   b   c   d

13. Rotate

a   b   c   d

14. Rotate

a   b   c   d

75

Test 16

Look at how the first two figures are changed, and then work out which option would look like the third figure if you changed it in the same way.

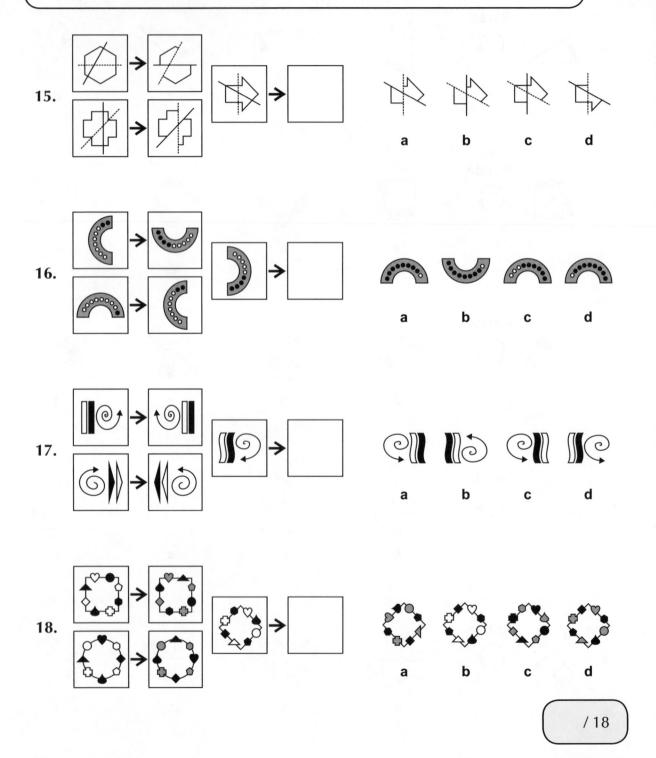

15.

a   b   c   d

16.

a   b   c   d

17.

a   b   c   d

18.

a   b   c   d

/ 18

Test 17

You have **10 minutes** to do this test. Circle the letter for each correct answer.

> Work out which option would look like the figure
> on the left if it was reflected over the line.

Reflect

1. |

                          a   b   c   d

Reflect

2. |

                          a   b   c   d

Reflect

3. |

                          a   b   c   d

Reflect

4. |

                          a   b   c   d

Reflect

5. |

                          a   b   c   d

      77   Test 17

Look at how the first bug changes to become the second bug. Then work out which option would look like the third bug if you changed it in the same way.

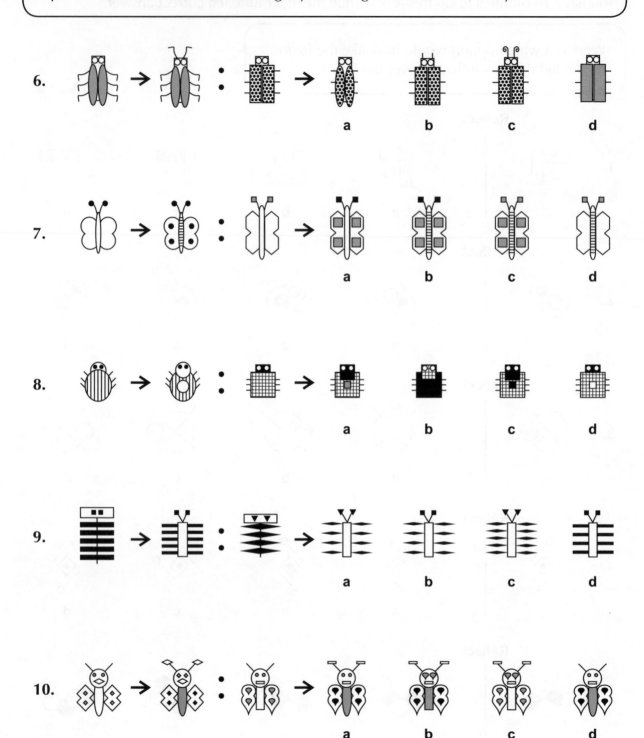

6.

a b c d

7.

a b c d

8.

a b c d

9.

a b c d

10.

a b c d

Work out which 3D figure in the grey box has been rotated to make the new 3D figure.

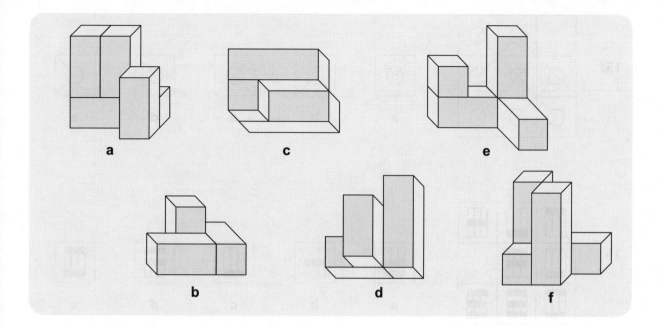

a

c

e

b

d

f

11.

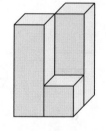

a   d

b   e

c   f

12.

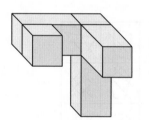

a   d

b   e

c   f

13.

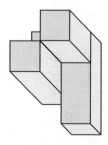

a   d

b   e

c   f

14.

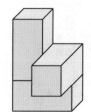

a   d

b   e

c   f

Test 17

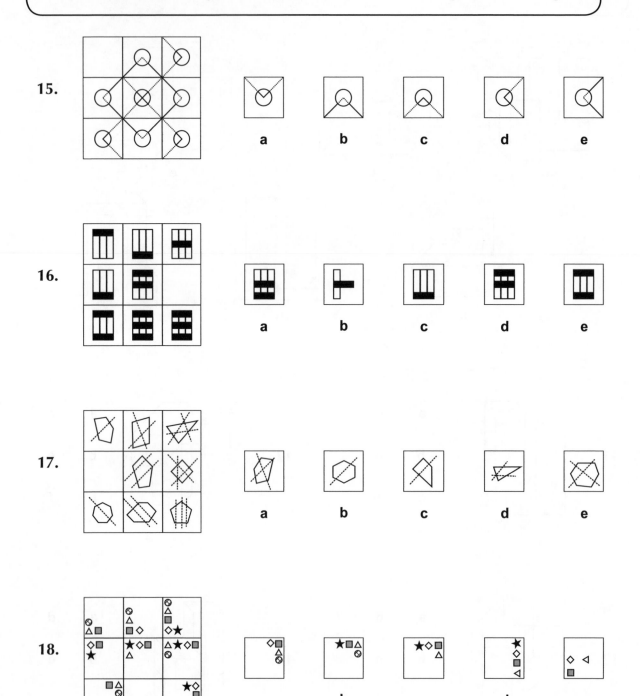

15. a b c d e

16. a b c d e

17. a b c d e

18. a b c d e

/ 18

80

You have **10 minutes** to do this test. Circle the letter for each correct answer.

Work out which set of blocks can be put together to make the 3D figure on the left.

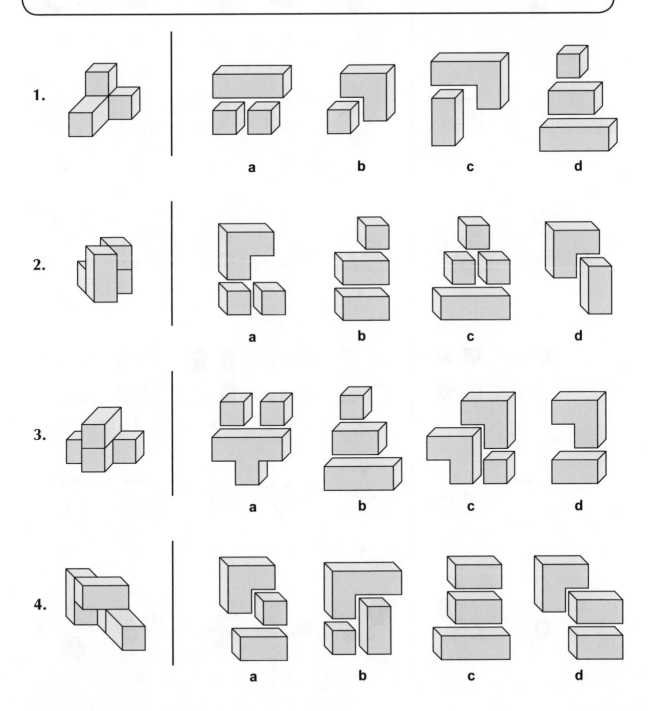

Work out which option is most like the two figures on the left.

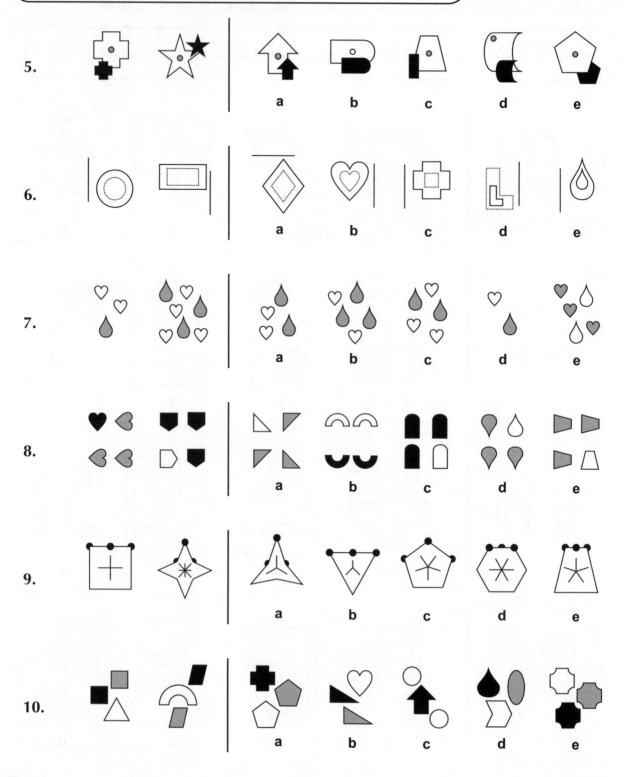

5.   a   b   c   d   e

6.   a   b   c   d   e

7.   a   b   c   d   e

8.   a   b   c   d   e

9.   a   b   c   d   e

10.   a   b   c   d   e

Work out which of the options best fits in place of the missing hexagon in the grid.

11.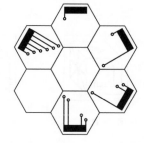

a   b   c   d

12.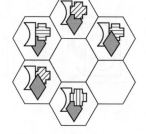

a   b   c   d

13.

a   b   c   d

14.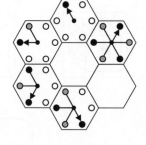

a   b   c   d

Test 18

Work out which of the four cubes can be made from the net.

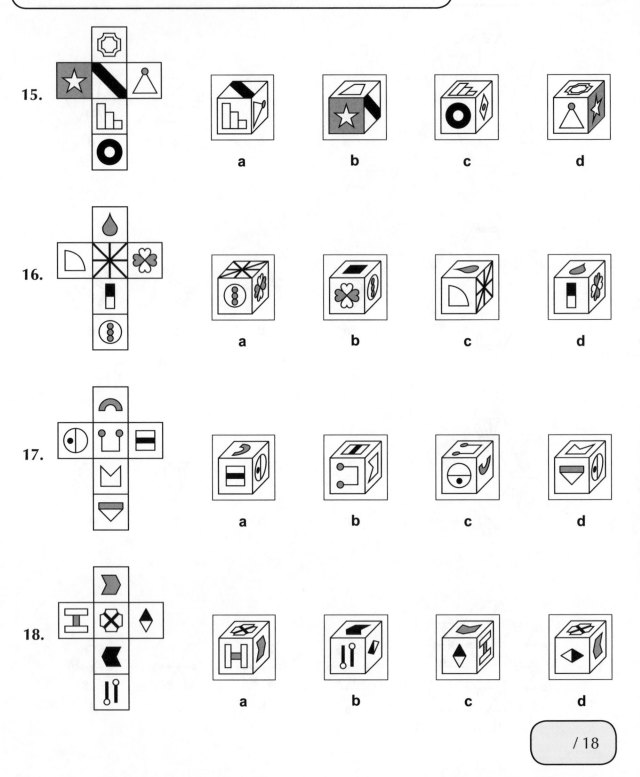

15.

a b c d

16.

a b c d

17.

a b c d

18.

a b c d

/ 18

84

Puzzles 6

Give these puzzles a go — they will help you with your **reflection** and **rotation** skills.

Peter the Painter

Peter is painting a palace which is standing on the shore of a lake.
What should the reflection of the palace in the lake look like in his painting?

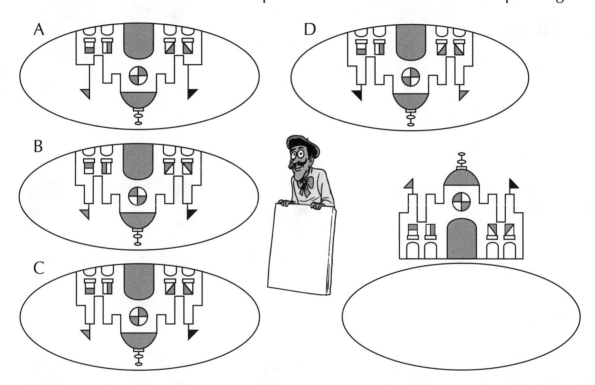

Let's Go Fly a Kite...

Anna and her three friends have very similar kites. Her dad takes a picture of their kites flying in the air. Which kite is Anna's?

Anna's kite

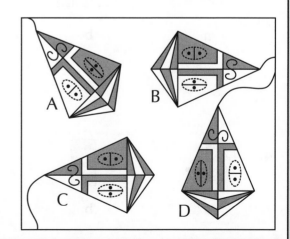

85

🕙 10

You have **10 minutes** to do this test. Circle the letter for each correct answer.

Find the figure in each row that is most unlike the others.

1.

    a   b   c   d   e

2.

    a   b   c   d   e

3.

    a   b   c   d   e

4.

    a   b   c   d   e

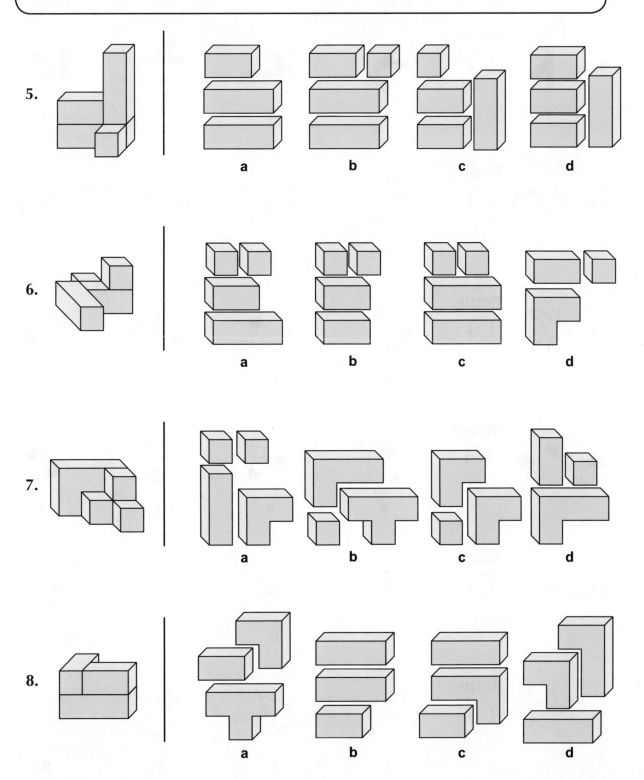

5.

a   b   c   d

6.

a   b   c   d

7.

a   b   c   d

8.

a   b   c   d

Work out which option would look like the figure on the left if it was rotated.

Rotate

9.

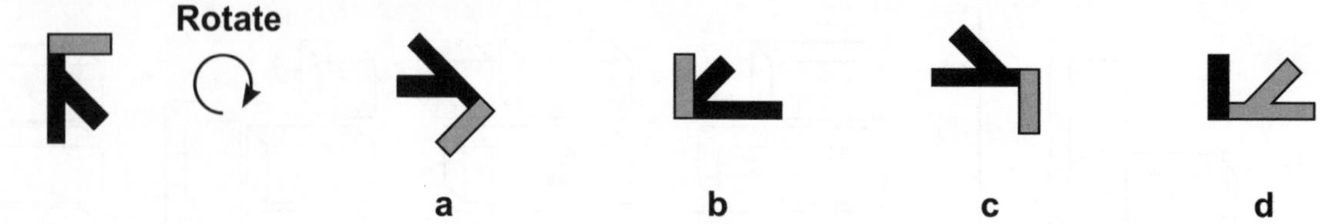

a   b   c   d

Rotate

10.

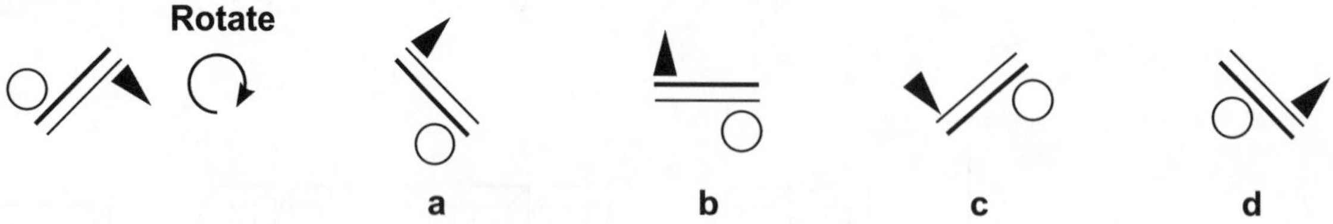

a   b   c   d

Rotate

11.

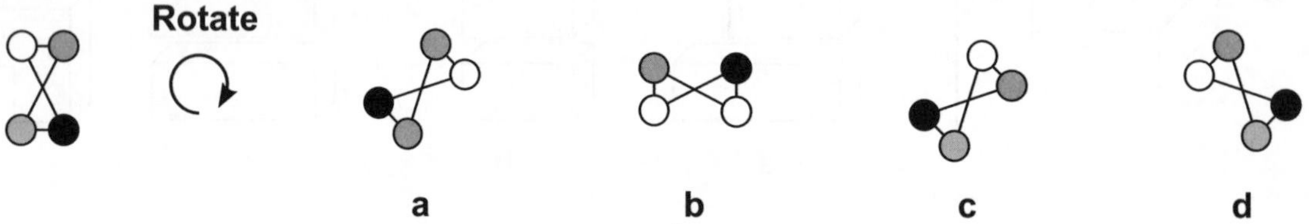

a   b   c   d

Rotate

12.

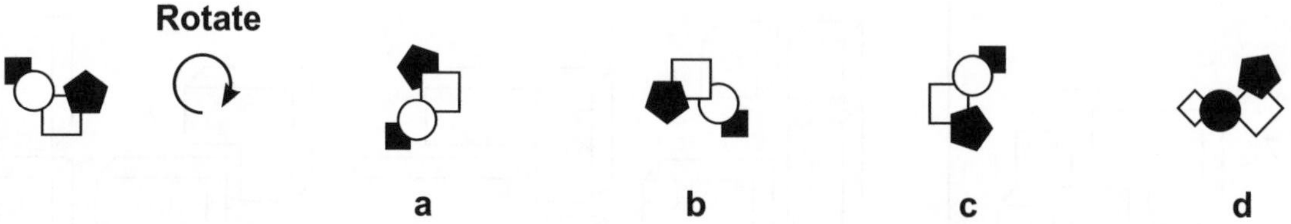

a   b   c   d

Rotate

13.

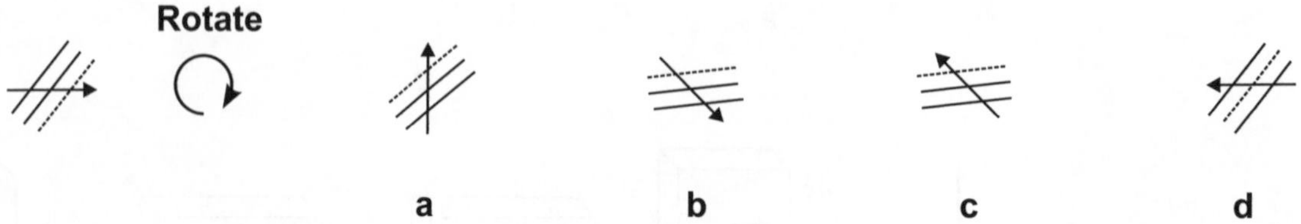

a   b   c   d

Rotate

14.

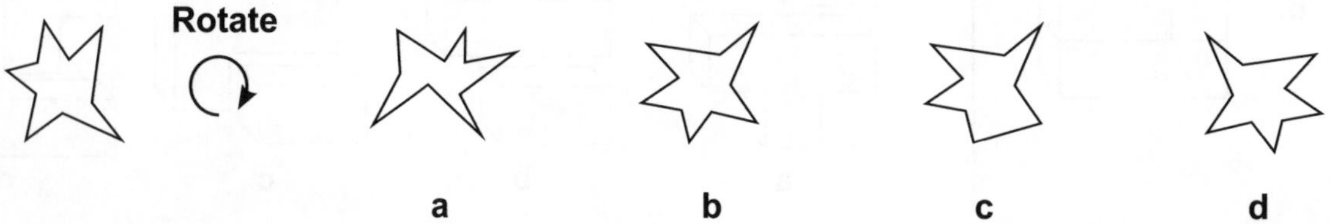

a   b   c   d

Look at how the first two figures are changed, and then work out which option would look like the third figure if you changed it in the same way.

15.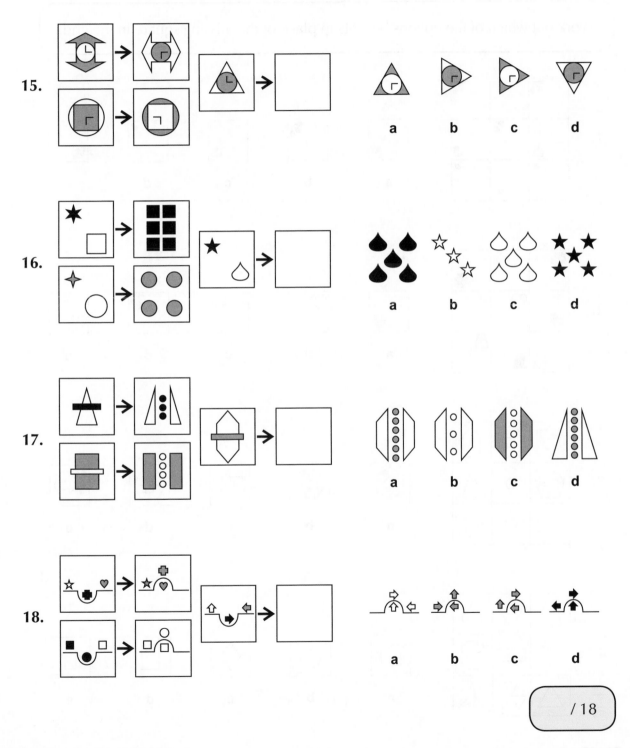

16.

17.

18.

/ 18

You have **10 minutes** to do this test. Circle the letter for each correct answer.

Work out which of the options best fits in place of the missing square in the grid.

1.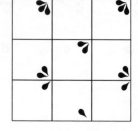

   a   b   c   d   e

2.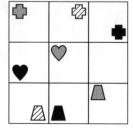

   a   b   c   d   e

3.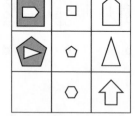

   a   b   c   d   e

4.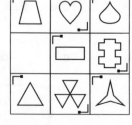

   a   b   c   d   e

Work out which of the four cubes can be made from the net.

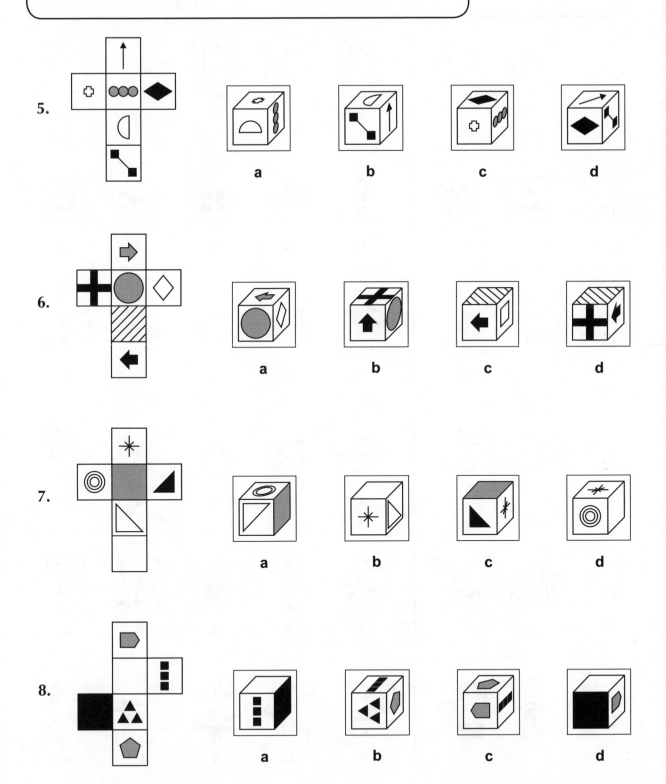

5.

a   b   c   d

6.

a   b   c   d

7.

a   b   c   d

8.

a   b   c   d

Test 20

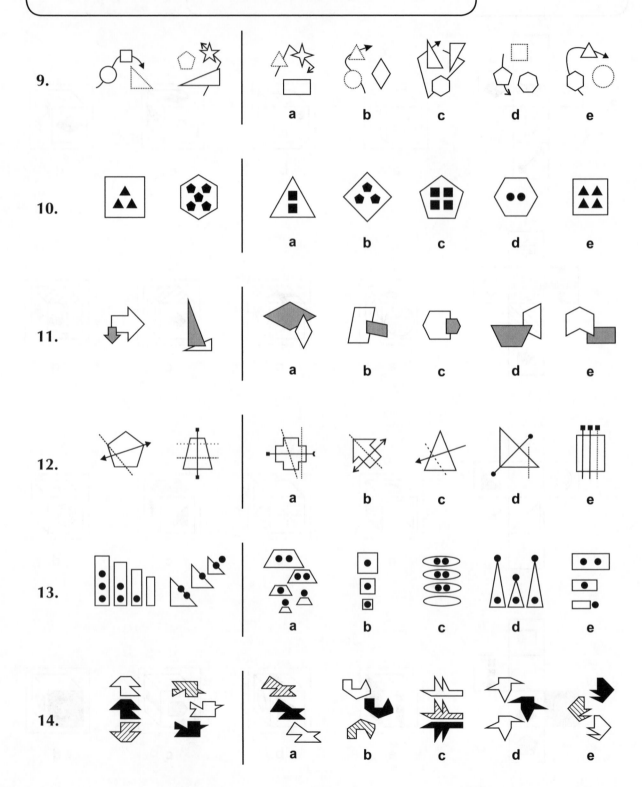

9.   a   b   c   d   e

10.   a   b   c   d   e

11.   a   b   c   d   e

12.   a   b   c   d   e

13.   a   b   c   d   e

14.   a   b   c   d   e

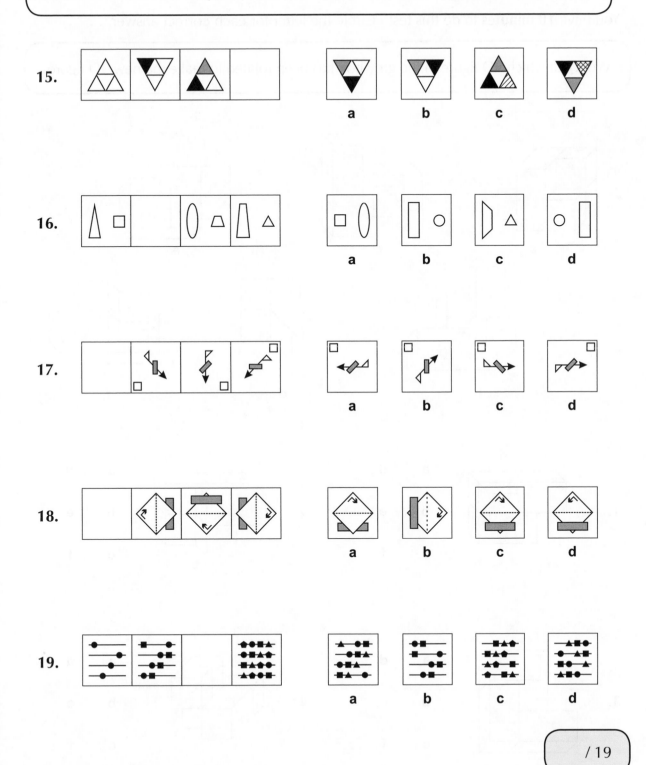

15.

a   b   c   d

16.

a   b   c   d

17.

a   b   c   d

18.

a   b   c   d

19.

a   b   c   d

/ 19

Test 20

You have **10 minutes** to do this test. Circle the letter for each correct answer.

Work out which 3D figure in the grey box has been rotated to make the new 3D figure.

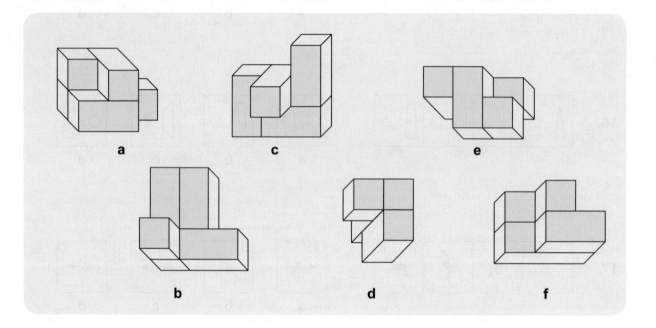

a   c   e

b   d   f

1.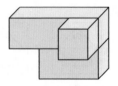

a   d

b   e

c   f

2.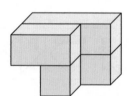

a   d

b   e

c   f

3.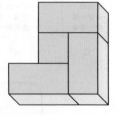

a   d

b   e

c   f

4.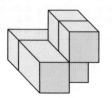

a   d

b   e

c   f

Work out which of the options best fits in place of the missing hexagon in the grid.

5.

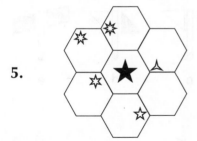

 a   b   c   d

6.

 a   b   c   d

7.

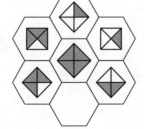

 a   b   c   d

8.

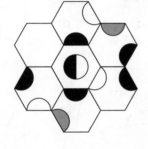

 a   b   c   d

Test 21

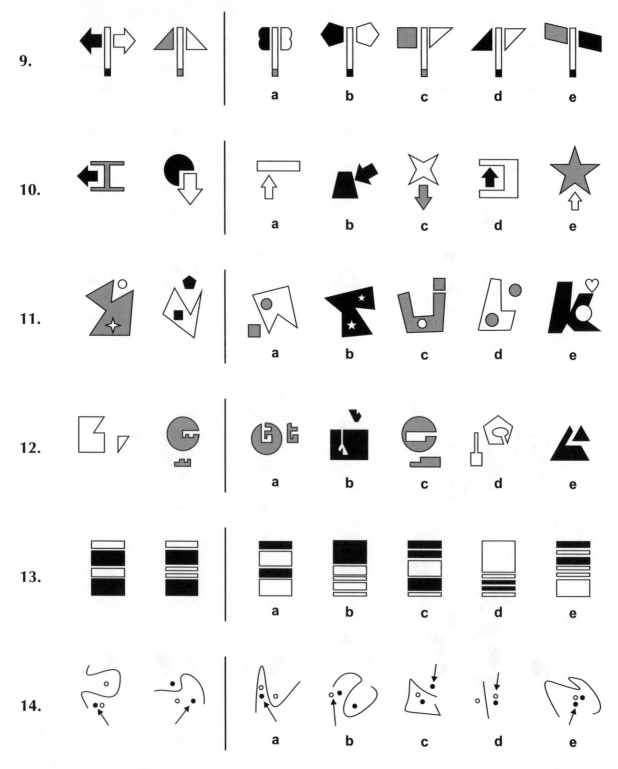

9.

10.

11.

12.

13.

14.

Work out which option would look like the figure on the left if it was reflected over the line.

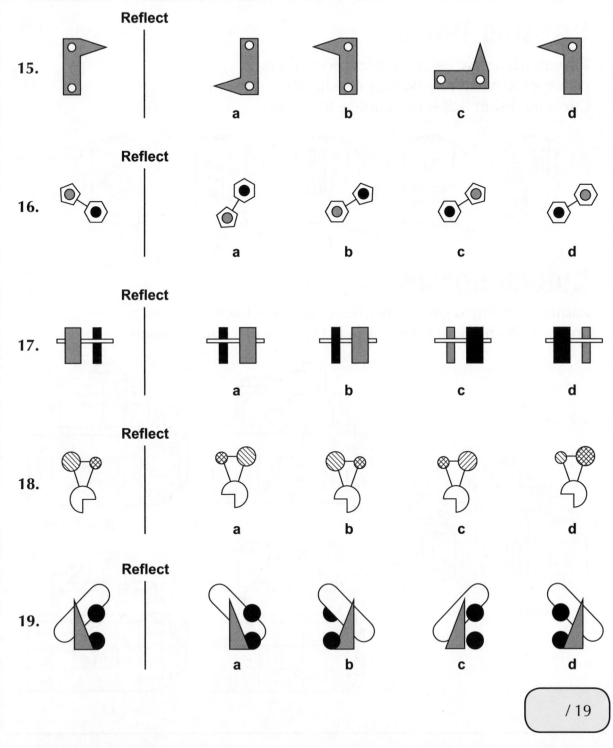

Reflect

15.   a   b   c   d

Reflect

16.   a   b   c   d

Reflect

17.   a   b   c   d

Reflect

18.   a   b   c   d

Reflect

19.   a   b   c   d

/ 19

Here's a puzzle page to put your **2D** and **3D shape** skills to the test.

Dressing Down

Clive needs a new T-shirt for the school disco.
He wants to make sure nobody else has the same one.
Circle the T-shirt that is most unlike the others.

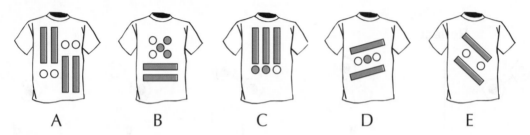

A   B   C   D   E

Hidden Houses

Rashina is trying to get into her house from the back, but she's
not sure which house is hers. Circle the back of Rashina's house.

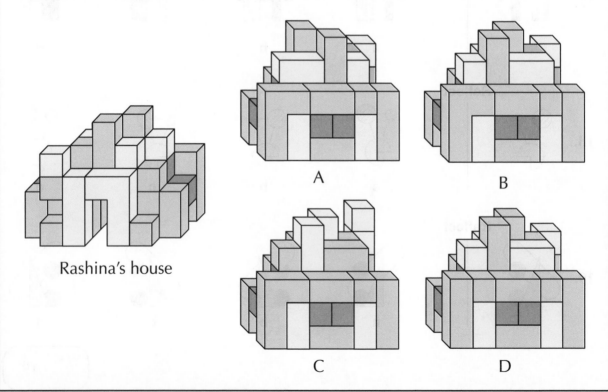

Rashina's house

A

B

C

D

98

Test 22

You have **10 minutes** to do this test. Circle the letter for each correct answer.

Work out which option is most like the three figures on the left.

1.

   a   b   c   d   e

2.

   a   b   c   d   e

3.

   a   b   c   d   e

4.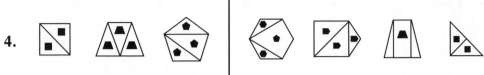

   a   b   c   d   e

5.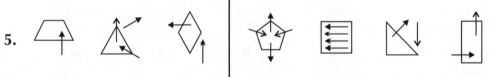

   a   b   c   d   e

© CGP — not to be photocopied   99   Test 22

Work out which of the options best fits in place of the missing hexagon in the grid.

6.

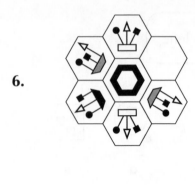

 a
 b
 c
 d

7.

 a
 b
 c
 d

8.

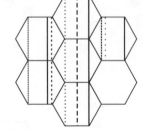

 a
 b
 c
 d

9.

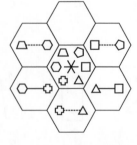

 a
 b
 c
 d

100

10.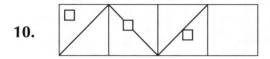

                               a   b   c   d

11.

                               a   b   c   d

12.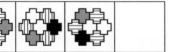

                               a   b   c   d

13.

                               a   b   c   d

14.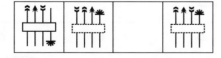

                               a   b   c   d

Test 22

Work out which option is a top-down 2D view of the 3D figure on the left.

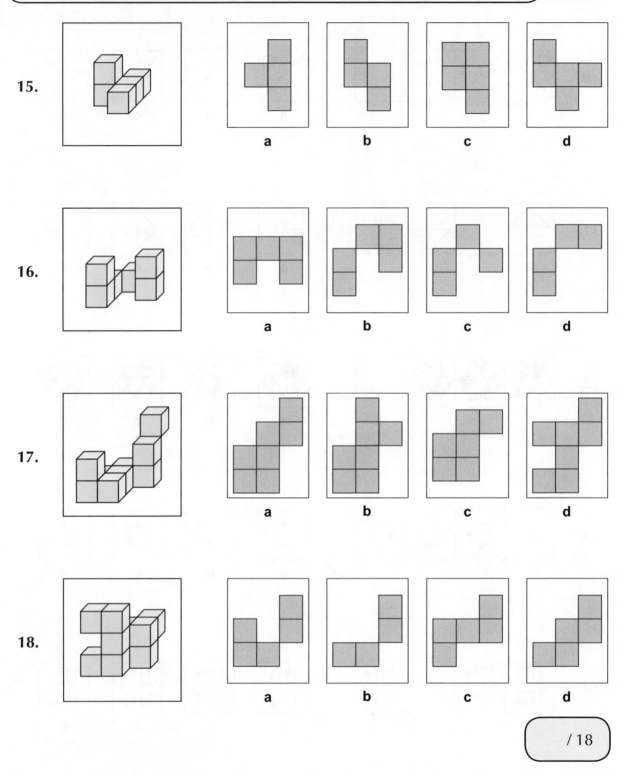

15.

a   b   c   d

16.

a   b   c   d

17.

a   b   c   d

18.

a   b   c   d

/ 18

You have **10 minutes** to do this test. Circle the letter for each correct answer.

> Look at how the first two figures are changed, and then work out which option would look like the third figure if you changed it in the same way.

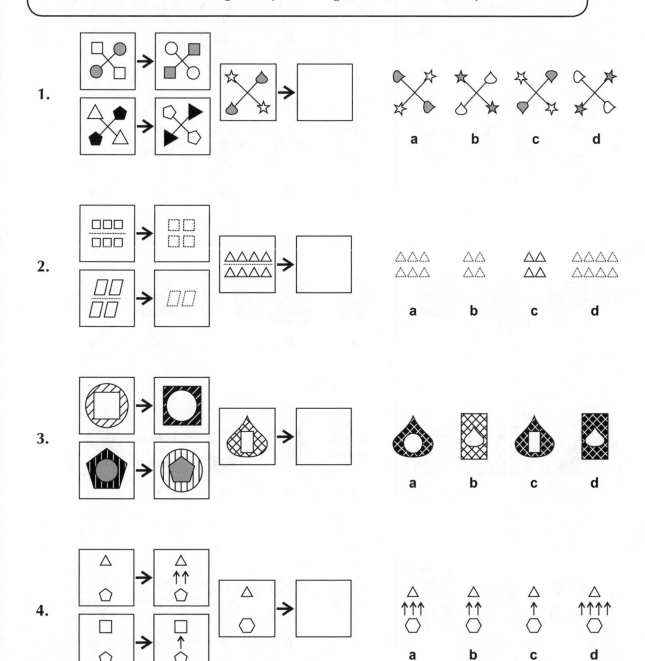

1.

a   b   c   d

2.

a   b   c   d

3.

a   b   c   d

4.

a   b   c   d

    103

Work out which option is most like the three figures on the left.

5.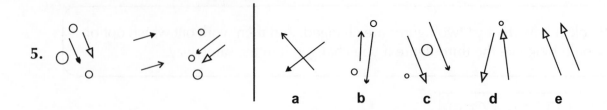

a   b   c   d   e

6.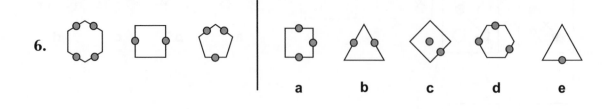

a   b   c   d   e

7.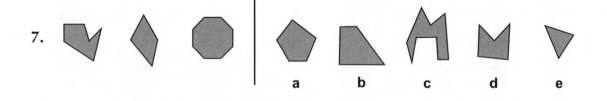

a   b   c   d   e

8.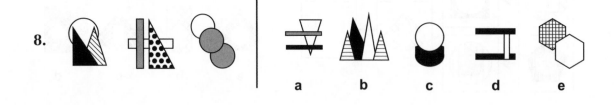

a   b   c   d   e

9.

a   b   c   d   e

Work out which 3D figure in the grey box has been rotated to make the new 3D figure.

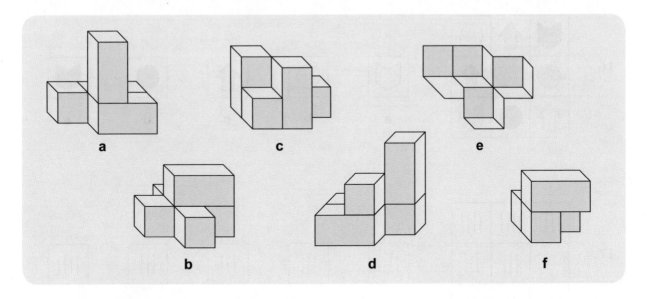

a

c

e

b

d

f

10.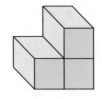

a	d
b	e
c	f

11.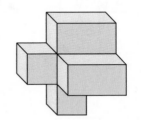

a	d
b	e
c	f

12.

a	d
b	e
c	f

13.

a	d
b	e
c	f

14.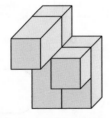

a	d
b	e
c	f

15.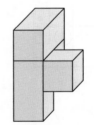

a	d
b	e
c	f

105

Work out which of the options best fits in place of the missing square in the grid.

16.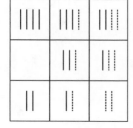

a   b   c   d   e

17.

a   b   c   d   e

18.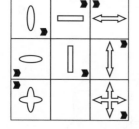

a   b   c   d   e

19.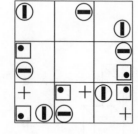

a   b   c   d   e

/ 19

Test 24

You have **10 minutes** to do this test. Circle the letter for each correct answer.

Work out which of the options best fits in place of the missing hexagon in the grid.

1.
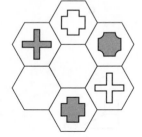

a b c d

2.
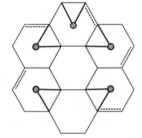

a b c d

3.
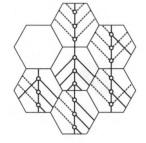

a b c d

4.

a b c d

Test 24

Work out which option would look like the figure on the left if it was rotated.

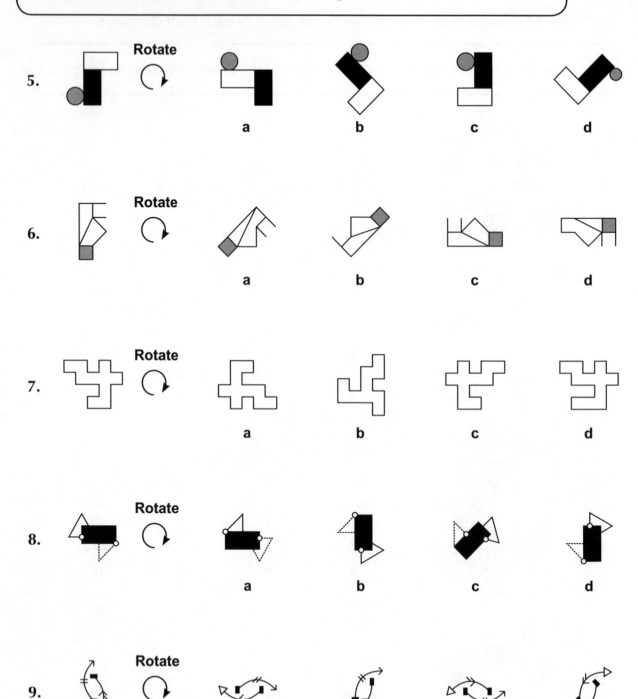

5.

Rotate

a   b   c   d

6.

Rotate

a   b   c   d

7.

Rotate

a   b   c   d

8.

Rotate

a   b   c   d

9.

Rotate

a   b   c   d

Find the figure in each row that is most unlike the others.

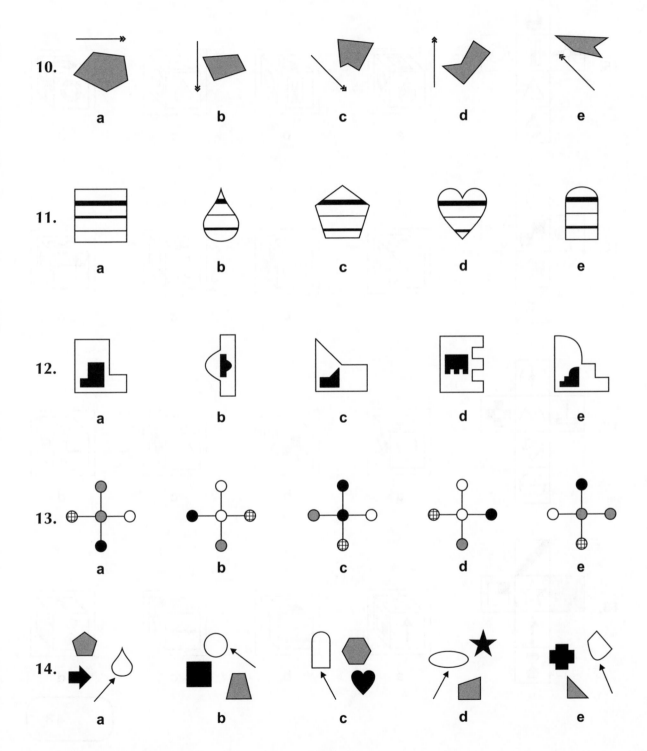

10.

a　　　b　　　c　　　d　　　e

11.

a　　　b　　　c　　　d　　　e

12.

a　　　b　　　c　　　d　　　e

13.

a　　　b　　　c　　　d　　　e

14.

a　　　b　　　c　　　d　　　e

109

Work out which of the four cubes can be made from the net.

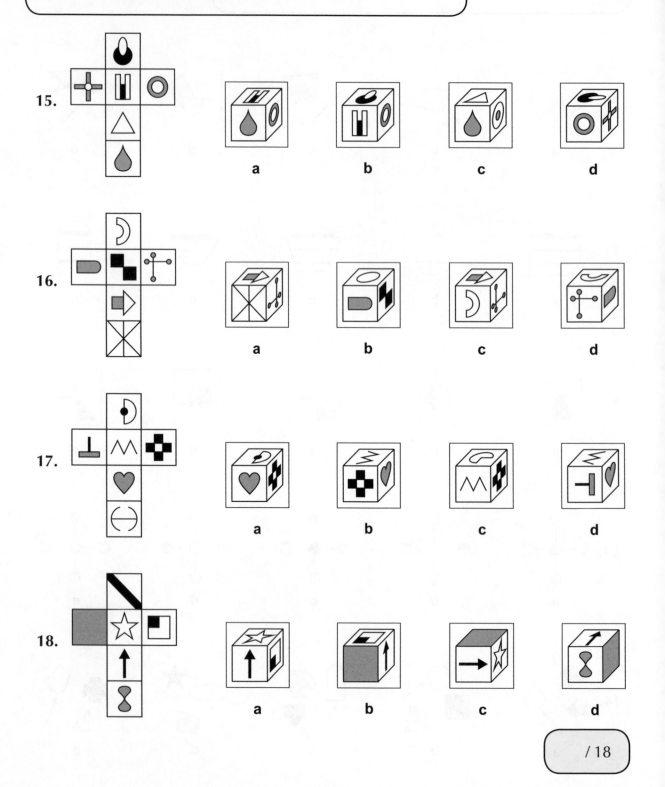

15.

a b c d

16.

a b c d

17.

a b c d

18.

a b c d

/ 18

110

Have a go at this puzzle and see how well you can **spot similarities** between things.

Leafy Logic

One leaf has fallen off each branch of Mr Gumpy's tree.
The leaves on each branch are similar to the other leaves on that branch.
Which branch (A-E) has each leaf (1-5) fallen from?

You have **10 minutes** to do this test. Circle the letter for each correct answer.

Work out which of the options best fits in place of the missing square in the series.

1.

a   b   c   d

2.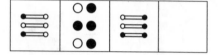

a   b   c   d

3.

a   b   c   d

4.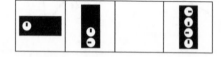

a   b   c   d

5.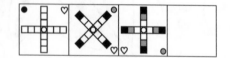

a   b   c   d

112

Work out which option is a top-down 2D view of the 3D figure on the left.

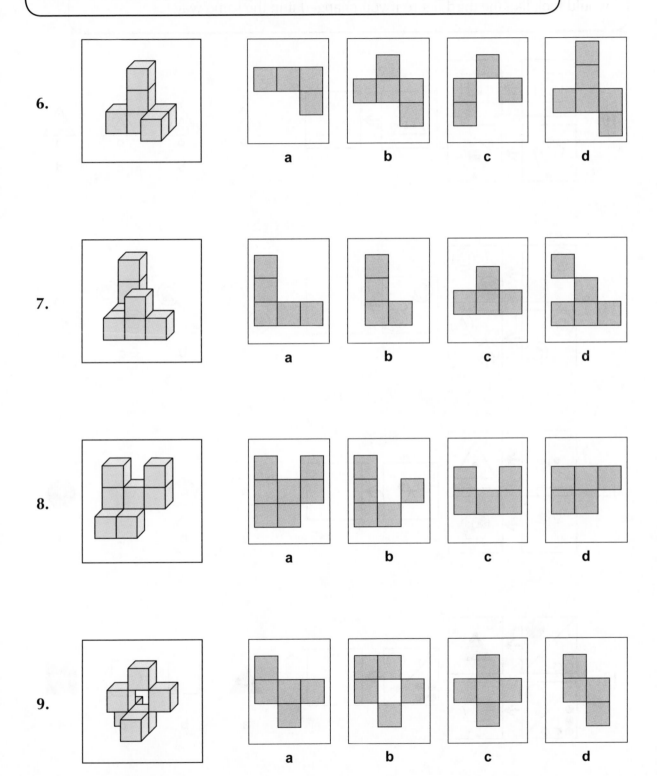

6.

a   b   c   d

7.

a   b   c   d

8.

a   b   c   d

9.

a   b   c   d

113

Look at how the first two figures are changed, and then work out which option would look like the third figure if you changed it in the same way.

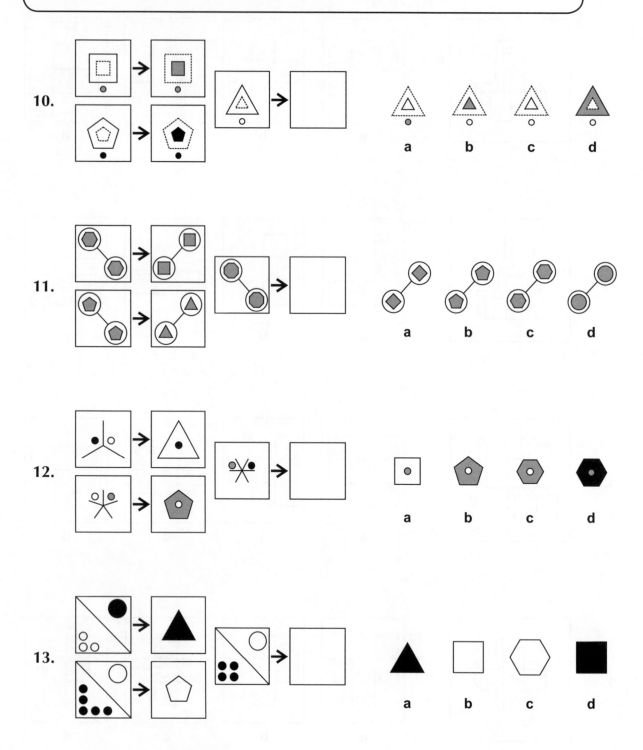

10.

a   b   c   d

11.

a   b   c   d

12.

a   b   c   d

13.

a   b   c   d

Work out which option would look like the figure on the left if it was reflected over the line.

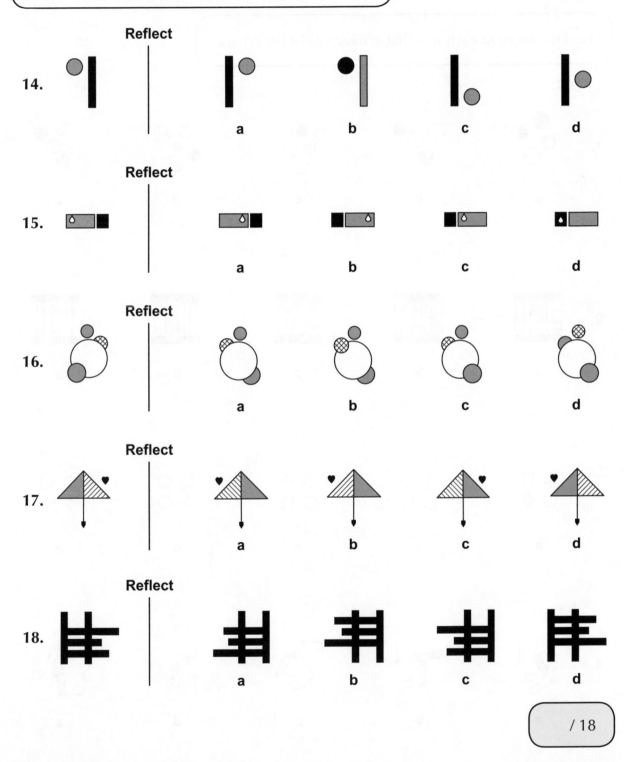

14.

Reflect

a　　　b　　　c　　　d

15.

Reflect

a　　　b　　　c　　　d

16.

Reflect

a　　　b　　　c　　　d

17.

Reflect

a　　　b　　　c　　　d

18.

Reflect

a　　　b　　　c　　　d

/ 18

115

You have **10 minutes** to do this test. Circle the letter for each correct answer.

Find the figure in each row that is most unlike the others.

1.

       a   b   c   d   e

2.

       a   b   c   d   e

3.

       a   b   c   d   e

4.

       a   b   c   d   e

Work out which option is most like the two figures on the left.

5.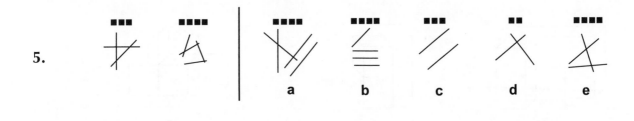

a   b   c   d   e

6.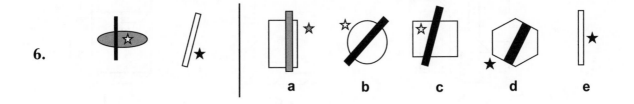

a   b   c   d   e

7.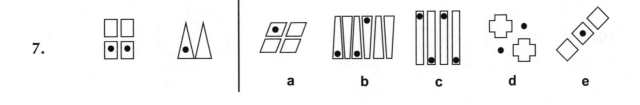

a   b   c   d   e

8.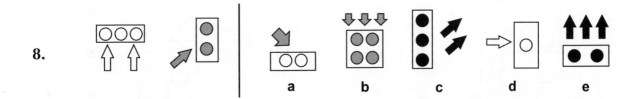

a   b   c   d   e

9.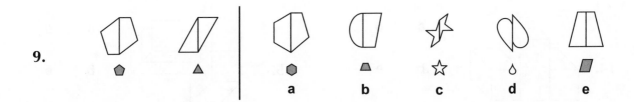

a   b   c   d   e

117

Work out which 3D figure in the grey box has been rotated to make the new 3D figure.

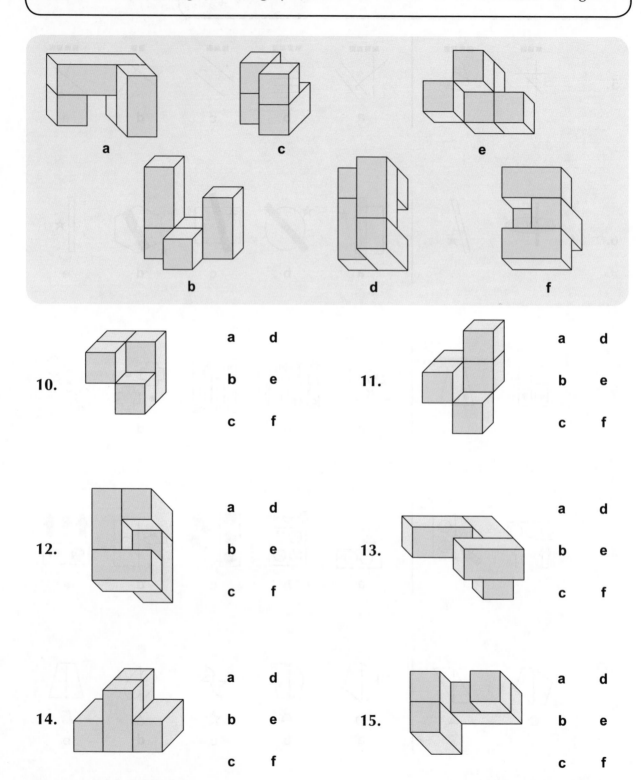

10.

a   d

b   e

c   f

11.

a   d

b   e

c   f

12.

a   d

b   e

c   f

13.

a   d

b   e

c   f

14.

a   d

b   e

c   f

15.

a   d

b   e

c   f

16.

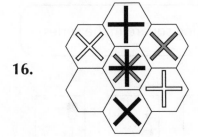

a   b   c   d

17.

a   b   c   d

18.

a   b   c   d

19.

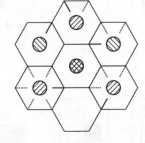

a   b   c   d

/ 19

You have **10 minutes** to do this test. Circle the letter for each correct answer.

Work out which of the options best fits in place of the missing square in the series.

1.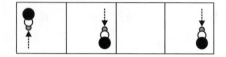

                a   b   c   d

2.

                a   b   c   d

3.

                a   b   c   d

4.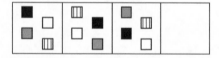

                a   b   c   d

5.

                a   b   c   d

Work out which set of blocks can be put together to make the 3D figure on the left.

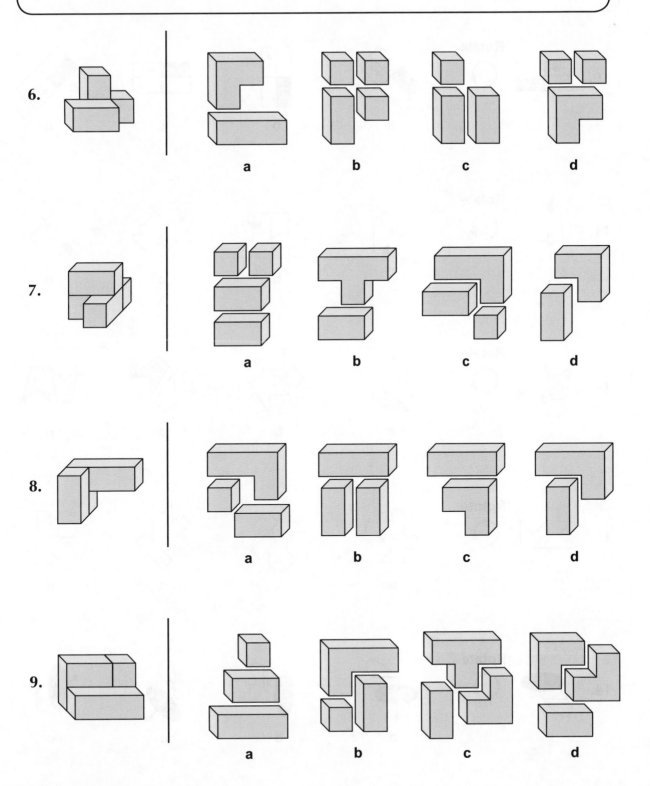

6.   a   b   c   d

7.   a   b   c   d

8.   a   b   c   d

9.   a   b   c   d

Work out which option would look like the figure on the left if it was rotated.

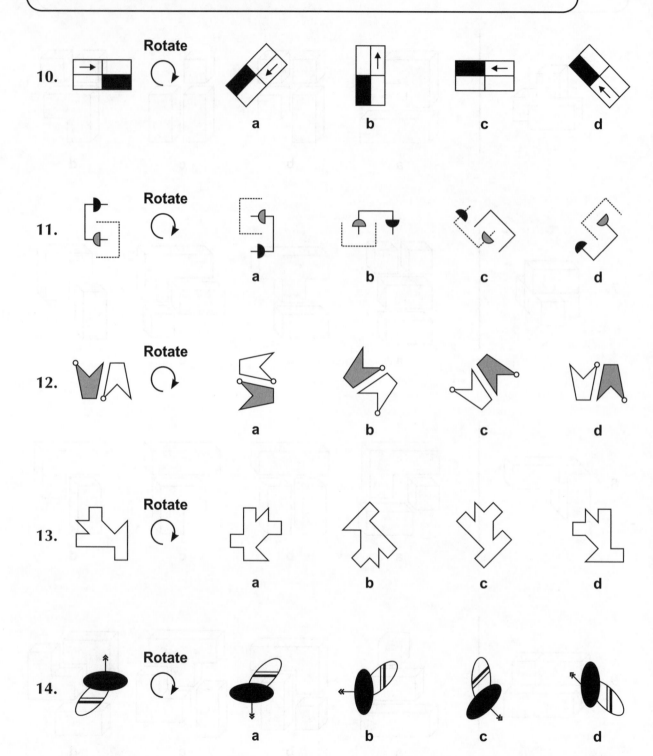

10. Rotate

a   b   c   d

11. Rotate

a   b   c   d

12. Rotate

a   b   c   d

13. Rotate

a   b   c   d

14. Rotate

a   b   c   d

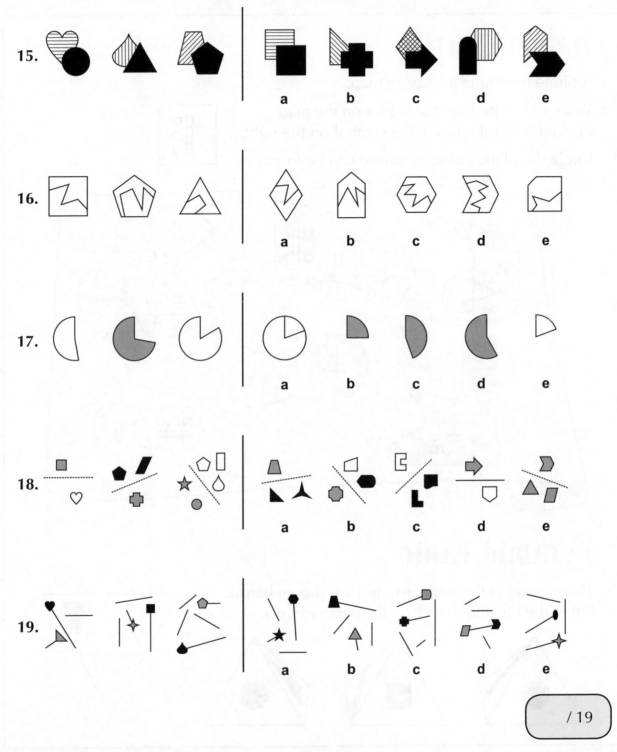

15.

a b c d e

16.

a b c d e

17.

a b c d e

18.

a b c d e

19.

a b c d e

/ 19

Puzzles 9

These puzzles are a fantastic way of practising the skills you'll need.

Mapped Out

A pirate has found a treasure map.

Treasure can be found at places on the map marked with rotations of the symbol on the right.

Circle the islands where treasure can be found.

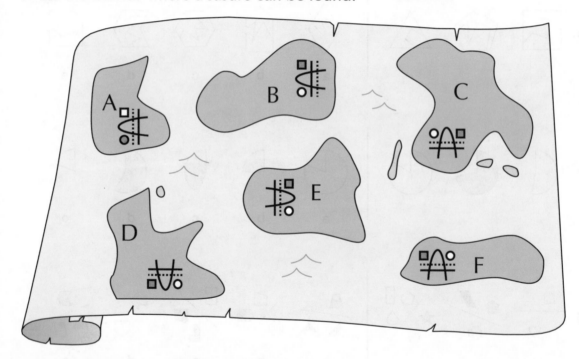

Pyramid Panic

Three views of the same pyramid are shown below.
Fill in the missing shapes on the pyramid's net.

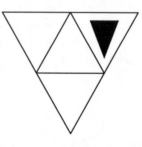

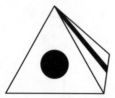
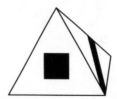
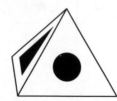

Test 28

You have **10 minutes** to do this test. Circle the letter for each correct answer.

Work out which of the options best fits in place of the missing square in the grid.

1.

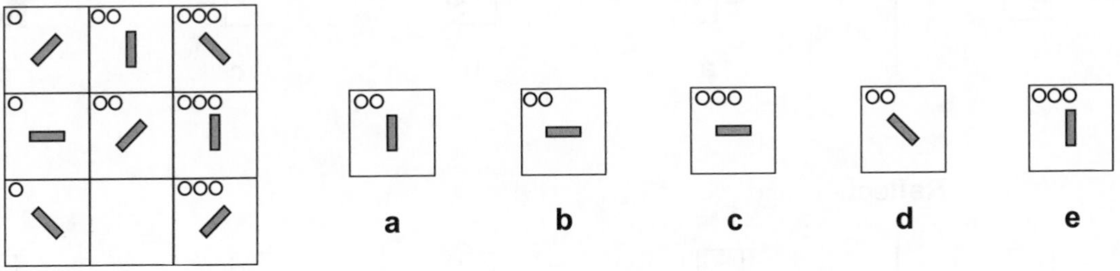
a
b
c
d
e

2.

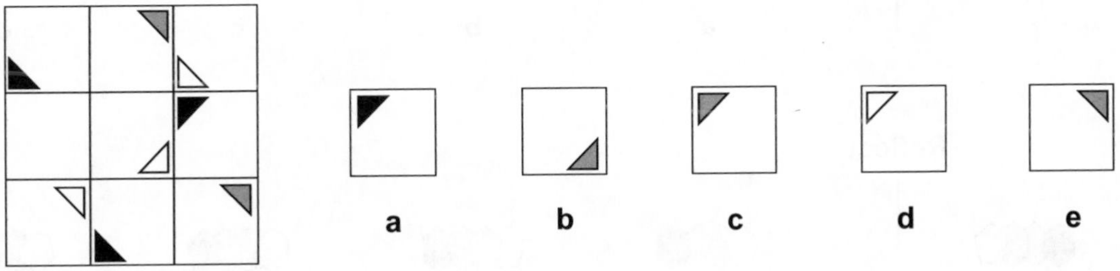
a
b
c
d
e

3.

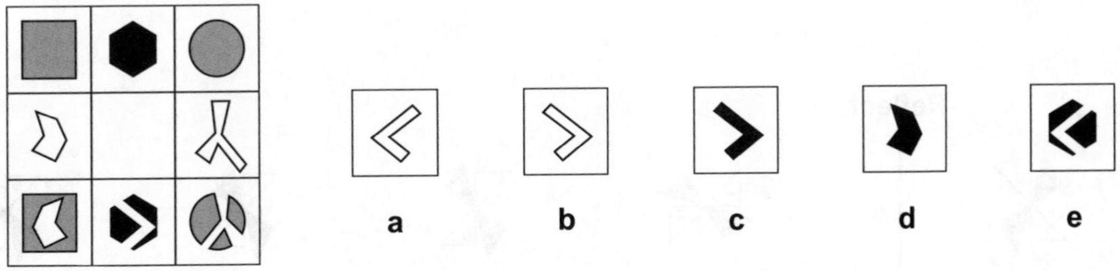
a
b
c
d
e

4.

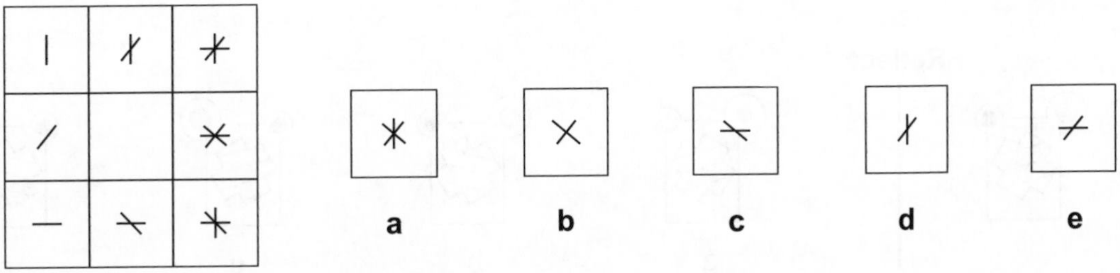
a
b
c
d
e

Work out which option would look like the figure
on the left if it was reflected over the line.

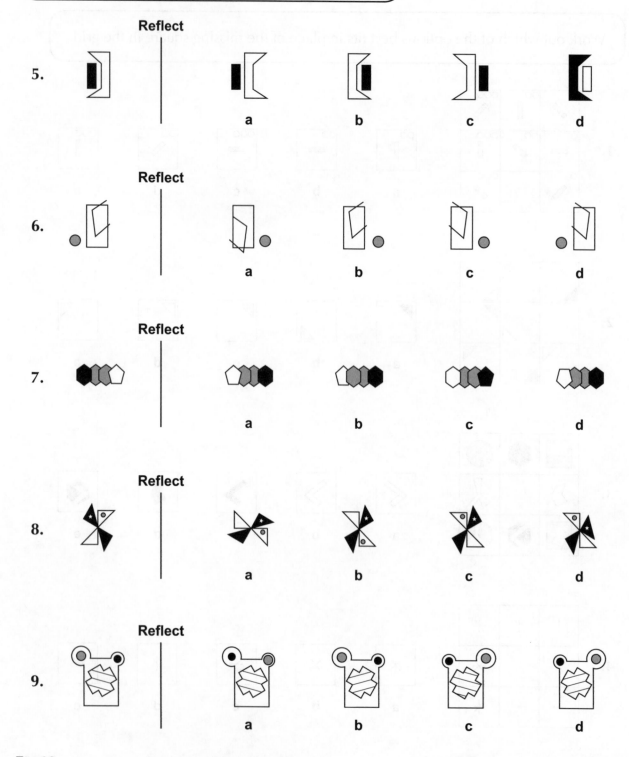

Reflect

5.

     a   b   c   d

Reflect

6.

     a   b   c   d

Reflect

7.

     a   b   c   d

Reflect

8.

     a   b   c   d

Reflect

9.

     a   b   c   d

Work out which option is a top-down 2D view of the 3D figure on the left.

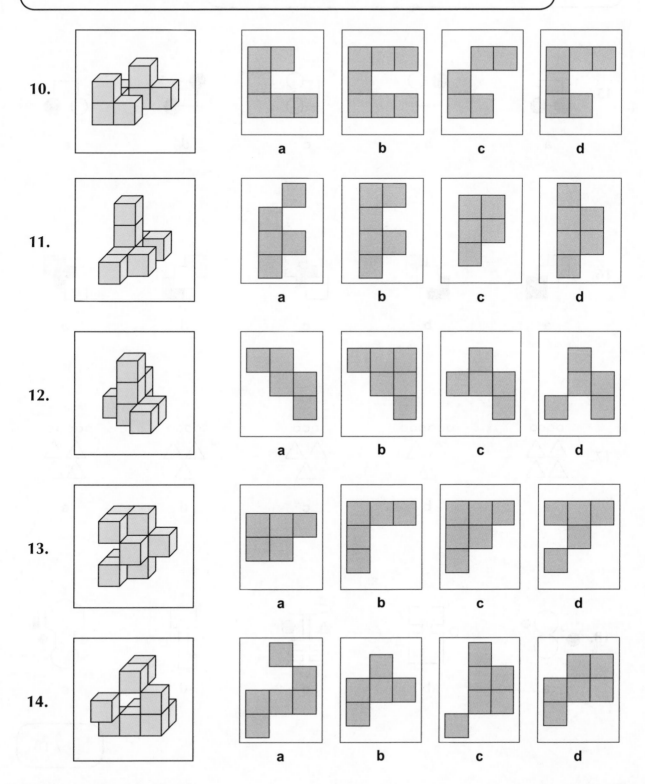

10. a b c d

11. a b c d

12. a b c d

13. a b c d

14. a b c d

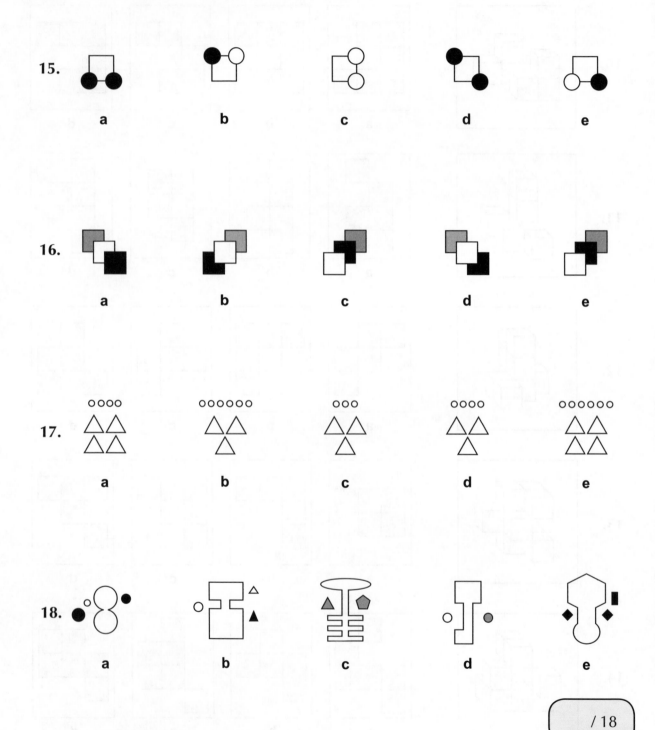

15.

a   b   c   d   e

16.

a   b   c   d   e

17.

a   b   c   d   e

18.

a   b   c   d   e

/ 18

You have **10 minutes** to do this test. Circle the letter for each correct answer.

Work out which 3D figure in the grey box has been rotated to make the new 3D figure.

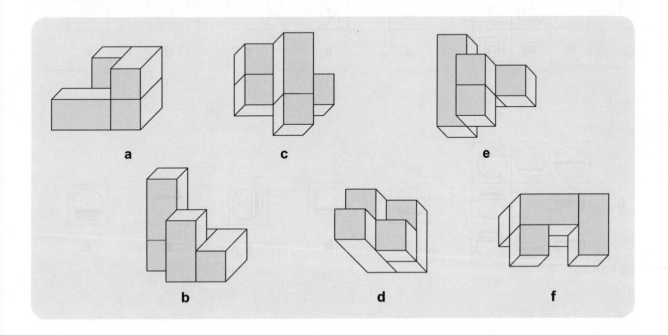

a   c   e

b   d   f

1.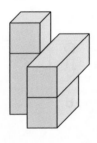

a	d
b	e
c	f

2.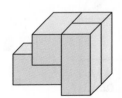

a	d
b	e
c	f

3.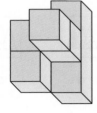

a	d
b	e
c	f

4.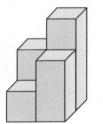

a	d
b	e
c	f

Work out which of the options best fits in place of the missing square in the grid.

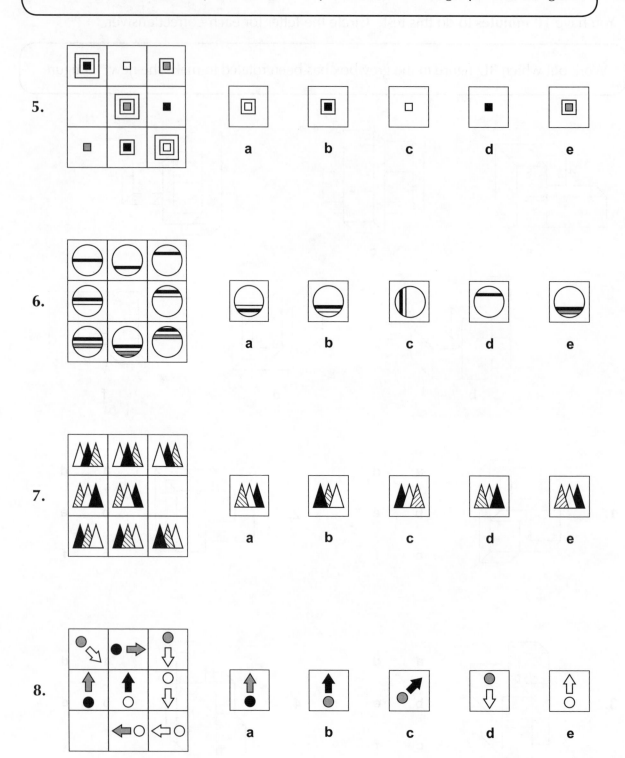

5.   a   b   c   d   e

6.   a   b   c   d   e

7.   a   b   c   d   e

8.   a   b   c   d   e

Look at how the first bug changes to become the second bug. Then work out which option would look like the third bug if you changed it in the same way.

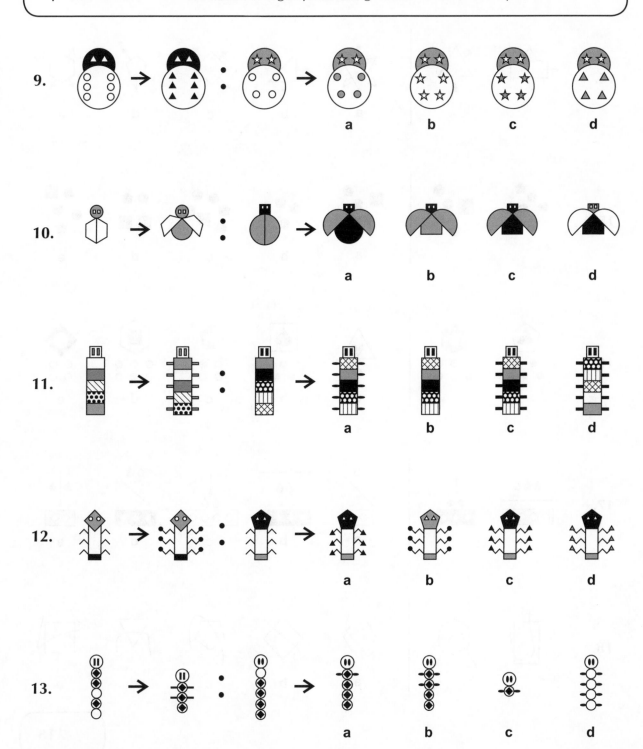

9.

10.

11.

12.

13.

131

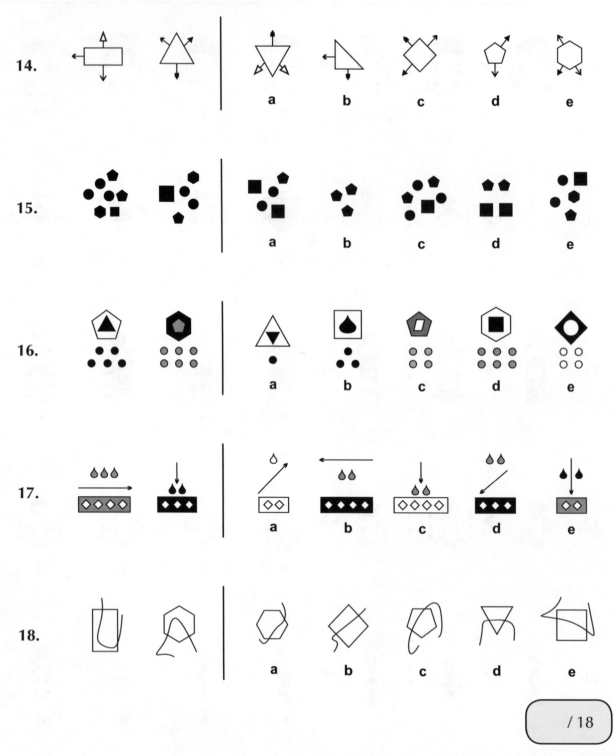

14.

a   b   c   d   e

15.

a   b   c   d   e

16.

a   b   c   d   e

17.

a   b   c   d   e

18.

a   b   c   d   e

/ 18

You have **10 minutes** to do this test. Circle the letter for each correct answer.

> Work out which option would look like the figure on the left if it was reflected over the line.

Reflect

1.

                               a   b   c   d

Reflect

2.

                               a   b   c   d

Reflect

3.

Reflect

4.

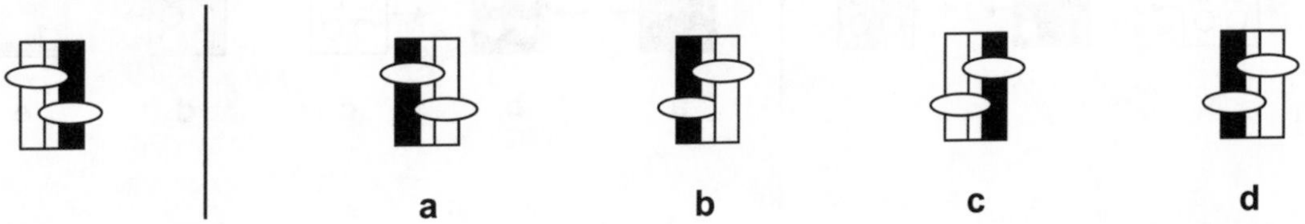

Reflect

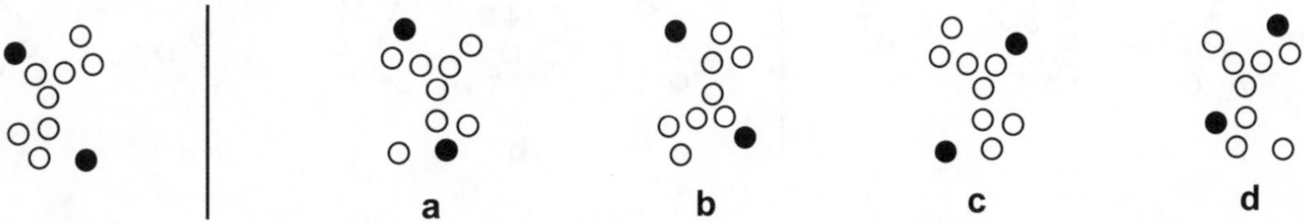

5.

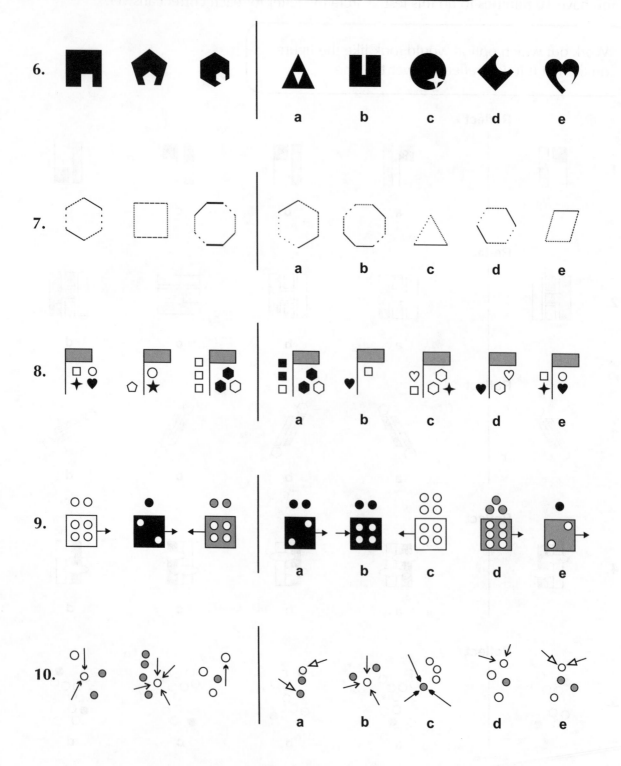

6.

7.

8.

9.

10.

Work out which of the options best fits in place of the missing square in the series.

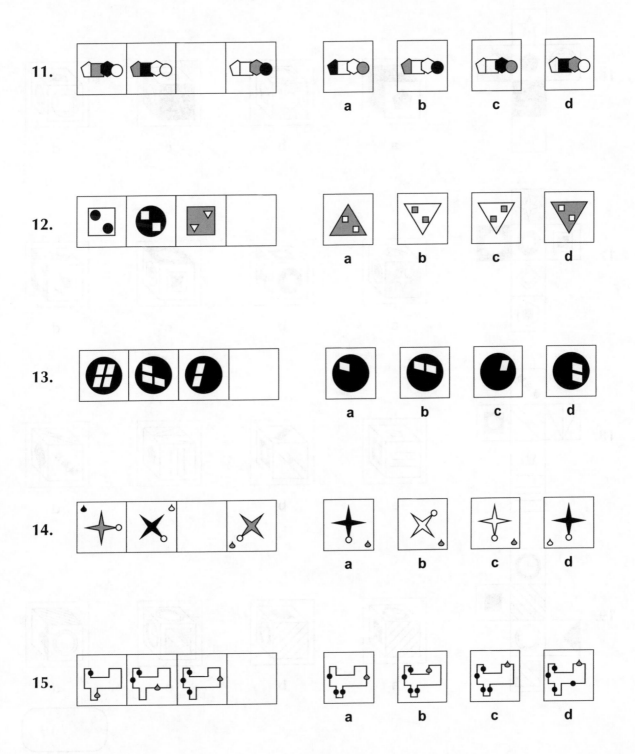

11.   a   b   c   d

12.   a   b   c   d

13.   a   b   c   d

14.   a   b   c   d

15.   a   b   c   d

Test 30

Work out which of the four cubes can be made from the net.

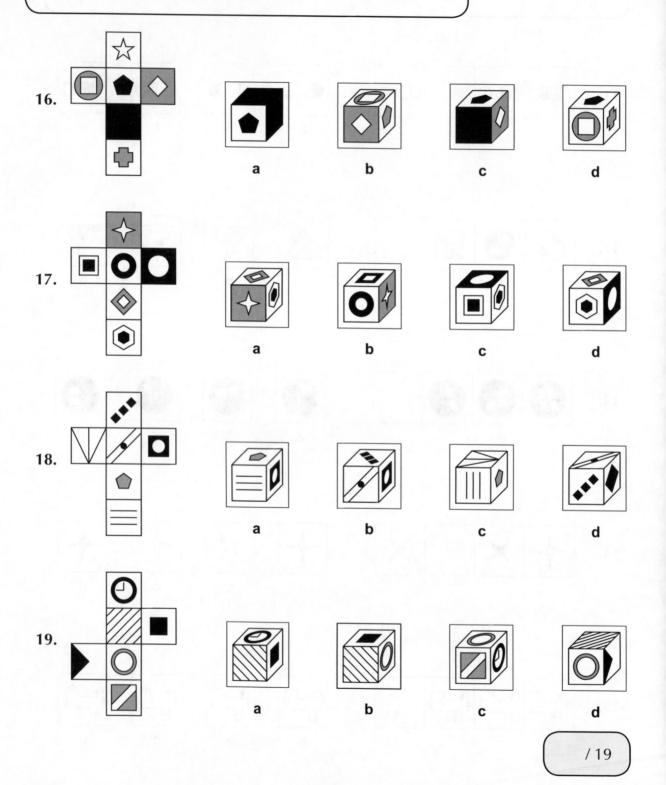

16.

a   b   c   d

17.

a   b   c   d

18.

a   b   c   d

19.

a   b   c   d

/ 19

Test 31

You have **10 minutes** to do this test. Circle the letter for each correct answer.

Work out which set of blocks can be put together to make the 3D figure on the left.

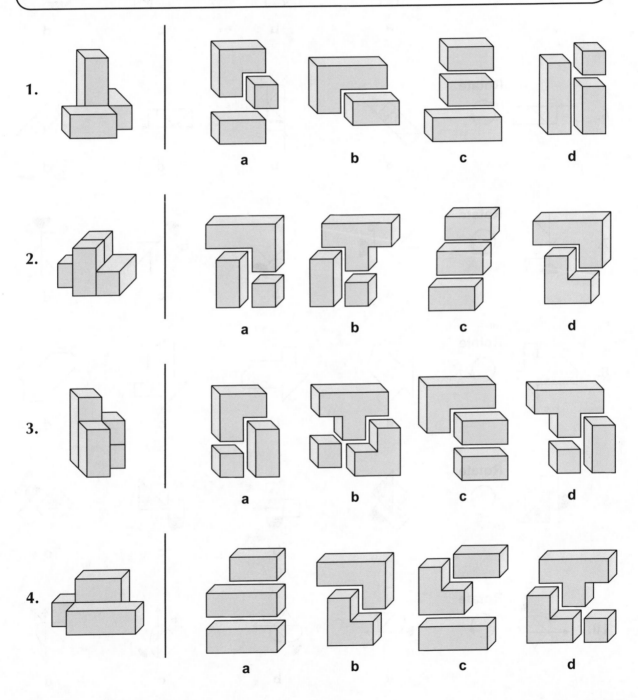

1.

a b c d

2.

a b c d

3.

a b c d

4.

a b c d

  137 Test 31

Work out which option would look like the figure on the left if it was rotated.

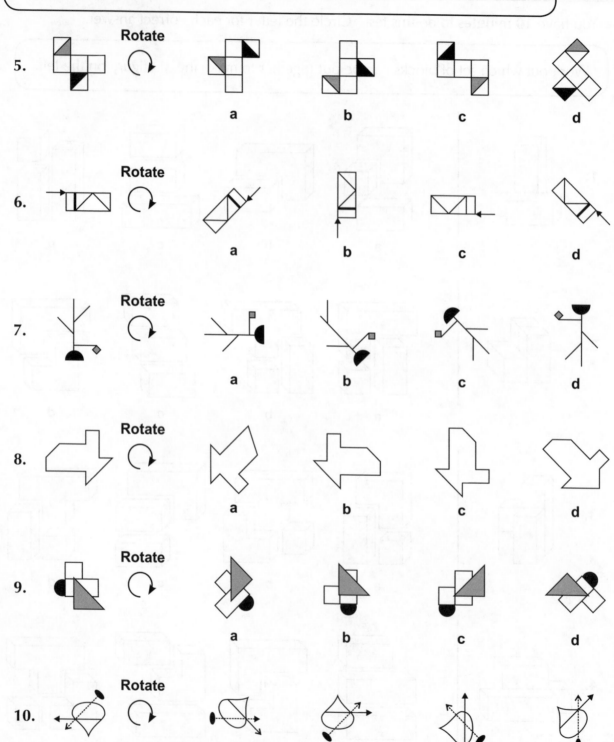

5. **Rotate**   a   b   c   d

6. **Rotate**   a   b   c   d

7. **Rotate**   a   b   c   d

8. **Rotate**   a   b   c   d

9. **Rotate**   a   b   c   d

10. **Rotate**   a   b   c   d

Look at how the first two figures are changed, and then work out which option would look like the third figure if you changed it in the same way.

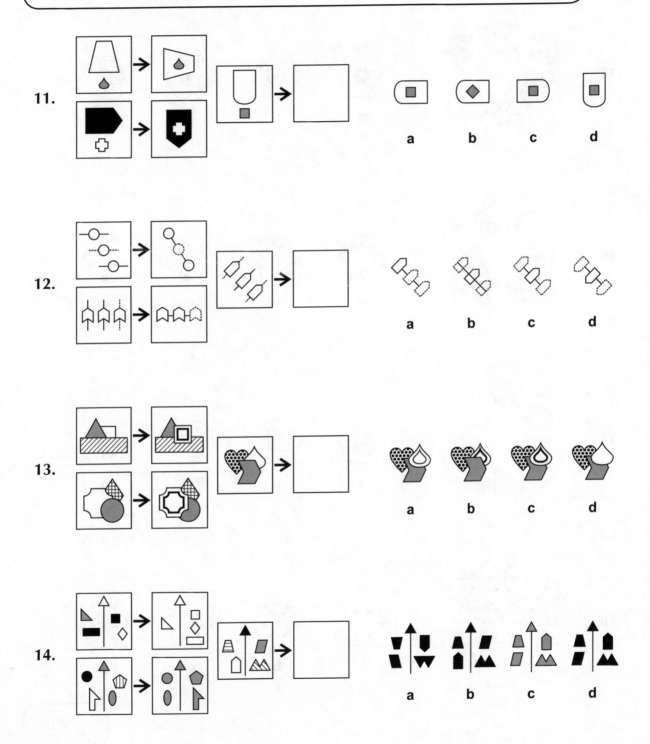

11.

a   b   c   d

12.

a   b   c   d

13.

a   b   c   d

14.

a   b   c   d

139

Test 31

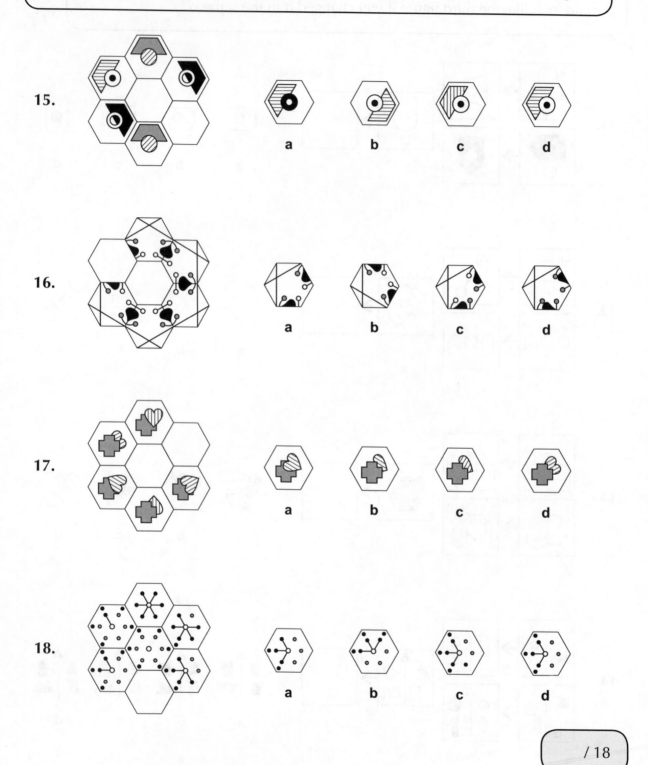

15.

a   b   c   d

16.

a   b   c   d

17.

a   b   c   d

18.

a   b   c   d

/ 18

You need to be able to rotate things in your head — here's a bit of fun practice for you.

Windmill Whirl

Billy has designed the paper windmill on the right.
A shape is punched through each sail.

Billy cuts along the dashed lines on the templates
below and folds each point to the centre.

Which template will make the windmill Billy designed?

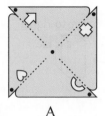 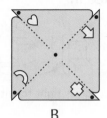 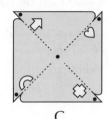 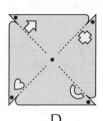 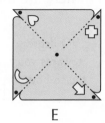

A	B	C	D	E

Animal Angles

Shefali has some tiles. On one side of each tile is a young creature.
On the other side of the tile is the matching adult creature.

She builds the shape in the box below using four tiles.
Which <u>two</u> of the figures below show Shefali's shape from different angles?

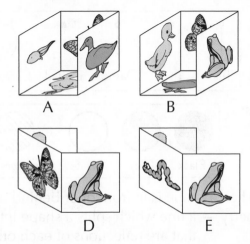

Glossary

Rotation and Reflection

Rotation is when a shape is turned clockwise or anticlockwise from its starting point.

Example shape

90 degree clockwise rotation

45 degree anticlockwise rotation

180 degree rotation

Reflection is when something is mirrored over an imaginary line.

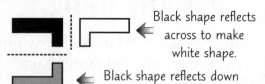

Black shape reflects across to make white shape.

Black shape reflects down to make grey shape.

3D Rotation

There are **three planes** that a 3D shape can be rotated in.

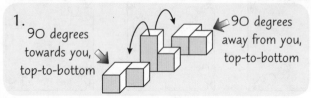

1. 90 degrees towards you, top-to-bottom

90 degrees away from you, top-to-bottom

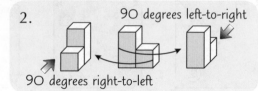

2. 90 degrees left-to-right

90 degrees right-to-left

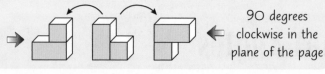

3. 90 degrees anticlockwise in the plane of the page

90 degrees clockwise in the plane of the page

Other Terms

Figure — the picture as a whole that makes up one example or option in a question.

Arrow-style Line — a line with a small shape at one end.

Line Types:

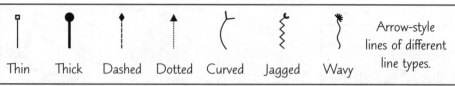

Thin   Thick   Dashed   Dotted   Curved   Jagged   Wavy

Arrow-style lines of different line types.

Shading Types:

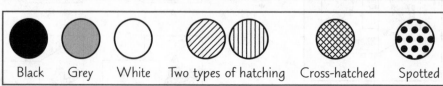

Black   Grey   White   Two types of hatching   Cross-hatched   Spotted

Layering — when a shape is in front of or behind other shapes.

Line of Symmetry — a line which splits a shape into halves that are reflections of each other.

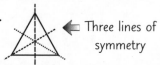

Three lines of symmetry

N6XPD2E2